Buckle Down™

Mississippi Algebra I

2nd Edition

This book belongs to: ________________________________

Helping your schoolhouse meet the standards of the statehouse™

ISBN 0-7836-5631-9

2BDMS10AG01 3 4 5 6 7 8 9 10

Senior Editor: Paul Meyers; Project Editor: Scott Johanningmeier; Editor: Tanya Burken; Production Editor: Jennifer Rapp; Cover Design: Christina Nantz; Cover Graphic Designer: Christina Kroemer; Production Director: Jennifer Booth; Art Director: Chris Wolf; Graphic Designer: Spike Schabacker; Composition: Wyndham Books.

TABLE OF CONTENTS

Table of Contents

To the Teacher:

Objective codes are listed for each lesson in the table of contents. The codes in the shaded gray bar that runs across the tops of the pages in the workbook show the Objective(s) covered on a given page (see example to the right). On some pages, Depth of Knowledge (DOK) levels appear in the shaded gray bar opposite the Objectives. DOK levels are assigned to the practice items on a given page.

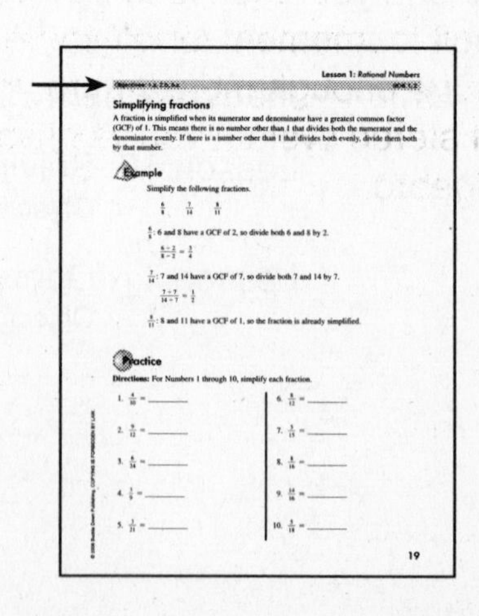

Lesson 1: *Rational Numbers*

Simplifying fractions

A fraction is simplified when its numerator and denominator have a greatest common factor (GCF) of 1. This means there is no number other than 1 that divides both the numerator and the denominator evenly. If there is a number other than 1 that divides both evenly, divide them both by that number.

Example

Simplify the following fractions.

$\frac{6}{8}$ $\frac{7}{14}$ $\frac{8}{11}$

$\frac{6}{8}$: 6 and 8 have a GCF of 2, so divide both 6 and 8 by 2.

$\frac{6 \div 2}{8 \div 2} = \frac{3}{4}$

$\frac{7}{14}$: 7 and 14 have a GCF of 7, so divide both 7 and 14 by 7.

$\frac{7 \div 7}{14 \div 7} = \frac{1}{2}$

$\frac{8}{11}$: 8 and 11 have a GCF of 1, so the fraction is already simplified.

Practice

Directions: For Numbers 1 through 10, simplify each fraction.

1. $\frac{4}{10}$ = ______
2. $\frac{9}{12}$ = ______
3. $\frac{6}{14}$ = ______
4. $\frac{3}{9}$ = ______
5. $\frac{3}{21}$ = ______
6. $\frac{8}{12}$ = ______
7. $\frac{5}{15}$ = ______
8. $\frac{8}{16}$ = ______
9. $\frac{14}{16}$ = ______
10. $\frac{3}{18}$ = ______

19

Introduction

Many people think of algebra as a classroom activity that is so abstract it has nothing to do with the real world. The truth is, algebraic concepts are at work all around you. The electronics you enjoy—such as CD and DVD players, video games, and computers—were made possible using principles of algebra. And it's not just high-tech businesses and products that rely on algebra. You will find algebra at work in almost any place where a product or service is provided. For example, behind the scenes at your favorite fast food restaurant or pizza place are people who rely on all kinds of algebra skills related to statistics, measurement, ratio and proportion, economics, graphing, and even probability to help them stay in business, make a profit, and make your lunch.

People use algebra skills in everyday life, too. If you double the size of a recipe, figure out how long it will take you and your friends to travel x miles to the state-basketball tournament, or estimate how long it will take you to save enough money from your part-time job to buy that stereo system you've always wanted, you are using algebra.

Test-Taking Tips

Here are a few general tips to keep in mind on test day.

TIP 1: Have the supplies you need.

For most math tests, you will need two sharp pencils and an eraser. Some tests will allow you to use scratch paper and/or a calculator to work your problems. Your teacher will tell you what you need for a test.

TIP 2: At test time, take it easy.

If you've practiced the material in this book, you will be better prepared to take the test. A little nervousness is natural and may actually help you stay aware and focused. Take a few deep breaths and think positively before you dive into the test.

TIP 3: Pace yourself.

Use your time wisely. It may be a good idea to first answer the easier items, then go back to the more difficult items. When you're finished, take a final flip through the test to see if you've left any blanks. If you still have blanks, try to answer the questions—do not leave any items blank.

TIP 4: Keep moving.

Work on a problem until you get stuck. Think about it for a couple of minutes and then move on to the other questions. Don't waste your time trying to figure out one question while you could be answering five other questions in the same time period.

TIP 5: Answer all multiple-choice items.

Every multiple-choice item has an answer. But if your answer doesn't match any of the answer choices, you may need to guess. Eliminate any unreasonable choices. If you are totally stumped, pick a letter and fill in one of the circles.

TIP 6: Check your work.

When you think you are finished with the test, use any remaining time to make sure you have answered all the questions. Check your answers for careless mistakes.

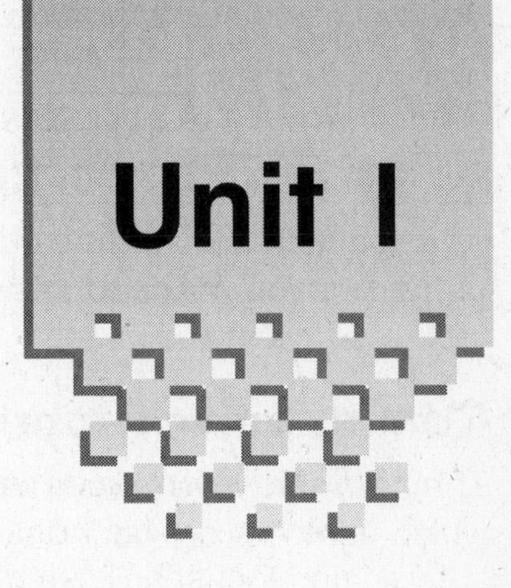

Number and Operations

You use numbers and operations almost every day. The designers of triangular roof trusses must be able to evaluate square roots of numbers to find the lengths of wood needed to build the trusses. Pluto is approximately $3.6 \bullet 10^9$ miles further from the Sun than Earth is. The total cost for 28 pens at $1.09 each is about $30.

In this unit, you will identify properties of the real number system and use them to simplify expressions. You will also compute with matrices and use them in problem-solving situations.

In This Unit

Number Concepts

Lesson 1: Number Concepts

In this lesson, you will review number properties and use them to simplify expressions. You will also use matrices to solve problems.

Number Properties

A **number property** states a relationship between numbers. Here are some number properties you will need to simplify expressions.

Commutative Property

The **commutative properties of addition and multiplication** state that the order in which numbers are added or multiplied does not matter.

$a + b = b + a$

$40 + 60 = 60 + 40$

$100 = 100$

$a \cdot b = b \cdot a$

$9 \cdot 7 = 7 \cdot 9$

$63 = 63$

Associative Property

The **associative properties of addition and multiplication** state that the way in which numbers are grouped (two at a time) when more than two numbers are added or multiplied does not matter.

$(a + b) + c = a + (b + c)$

$(8 + 5) + 4 = 8 + (5 + 4)$

$13 + 4 = 8 + 9$

$17 = 17$

$(a \cdot b) \cdot c = a \cdot (b \cdot c)$

$(6 \cdot 3) \cdot 2 = 6 \cdot (3 \cdot 2)$

$18 \cdot 2 = 6 \cdot 6$

$36 = 36$

Distributive Property

The **distributive property** relates multiplication to addition or subtraction. The property states that everything inside the parentheses is multiplied by whatever is outside the parentheses.

$a(b + c) = a \cdot b + a \cdot c$

$10(4 + 1) = 10 \cdot 4 + 10 \cdot 1$

$10(5) = 40 + 10$

$50 = 50$

$a(b - c) = a \cdot b - a \cdot c$

$6(3 - 2) = 6 \cdot 3 - 6 \cdot 2$

$6(1) = 18 - 12$

$6 = 6$

Objectives: 1a

Simplifying Expressions

To simplify an algebraic expression, you need to combine the **like terms**. Like terms have the same variables with the same exponents. If two terms are like terms, then only their coefficients may differ. Once you find all the like terms, you can combine them by adding or subtracting the coefficients only.

Example

Simplify the following expression.

$4(z - 17) + 11z - 6 + 2z^2$

Use the distributive property to simplify the part of the expression with parentheses.

$4(z - 17) + 11z - 6 + 2z^2$

$4 \bullet z - 4 \bullet 17 + 11z - 6 + 2z^2$

$4z - 68 + 11z - 6 + 2z^2$

Use the commutative property to rewrite the expression so that like terms are next to each other and the exponents decrease in order.

$4z - 68 + 11z - 6 + 2z^2$

$2z^2 + 4z + 11z - 68 - 6$

Use the associative property to regroup the addition and subtraction and simplify the like terms.

$2z^2 + (4z + 11z) + (-68 - 6)$

$2z^2 + 15z - 74$

Practice

Directions: For Numbers 1 through 12, simplify each expression.

1. $4a - 17 + 6(a - 3)$

2. $-9f + 7f - 17$

3. $12x - 4 + 6 - 19x$

4. $6(y + 12)$

5. $-4(p - 6) + 19$

6. $4x^2 + 3y + 7 - 3x^2$

7. $6h + 6 - 8h$

8. $-12x^2 + 13x + 3x - 2$

9. $6y + 3y + 3$

10. $8z^2 + 7z + 6z^2 + 8(y + 9)$

11. $-4p + 2p^2 + 6$

12. $6 + 4j^2 + 2k + 3j - 6j^2$

Objectives: 1b

Matrices

A **matrix** is a rectangular array of numbers. Most applications of **matrices** (the plural form of matrix) occur in the areas of the social and physical sciences. This lesson will concentrate on the correct use of the matrix operations of addition, subtraction, and scalar multiplication.

Matrix Addition

In order to add two matrices, they must be of the same **order** (have the same number of rows and columns). The sum of the matrices is a matrix of the same order. The elements of the new matrix are found by adding the corresponding elements of the original matrices.

Example

$$\begin{bmatrix} 3 & 4 & -8 \\ -8 & 1 & 0 \end{bmatrix} + \begin{bmatrix} 7 & -2 & 9 \\ -4 & -9 & 3 \end{bmatrix} = \begin{bmatrix} 3+7 & 4+(-2) & -8+9 \\ -8+(-4) & 1+(-9) & 0+3 \end{bmatrix}$$

$$= \begin{bmatrix} 10 & 2 & 1 \\ -12 & -8 & 3 \end{bmatrix}$$

Example

$$\begin{bmatrix} 5 & 8 \\ -5 & 4 \\ 9 & -4 \end{bmatrix} + \begin{bmatrix} -5 & 2 \\ 3 & 8 \\ -2 & 0 \end{bmatrix} = \begin{bmatrix} 5+(-5) & 8+2 \\ -5+3 & 4+8 \\ 9+(-2) & -4+0 \end{bmatrix}$$

$$= \begin{bmatrix} 0 & 10 \\ -2 & 12 \\ 7 & -4 \end{bmatrix}$$

TIP: The matrices in the first example are both 2×3 (read "2 by 3"). The matrices in the second example are both 3×2 (read "3 by 2"). The elements of a matrix are identified by their position in rows and columns. In the answer to the second example, the 7 is in row 3, column 1, so its position is 3, 1.

Practice

Directions: For Numbers 1 through 4, add the matrices.

1. $\begin{bmatrix} 6 & 4 & -8 \\ -8 & 6 & -7 \\ 2 & 4 & 3 \\ 3 & -8 & -4 \end{bmatrix} + \begin{bmatrix} -4 & 6 & -2 \\ -1 & 0 & 8 \\ 8 & 4 & 8 \\ -3 & 4 & 0 \end{bmatrix} =$

2. $\begin{bmatrix} 2 & 8 & 7 & 4 \\ 9 & 8 & 4 & 2 \end{bmatrix} + \begin{bmatrix} 9 & -5 & 4 & 2 \\ -7 & 0 & 5 & 2 \end{bmatrix} =$

3. $\begin{bmatrix} -5 & 8 \\ 3 & 7 \\ 3 & 5 \\ -3 & -7 \\ 3 & 7 \end{bmatrix} + \begin{bmatrix} 6 & -4 \\ -8 & -1 \\ 8 & -1 \\ 8 & 4 \\ 8 & 4 \end{bmatrix} =$

4. $\begin{bmatrix} 2 & 8 & 7 & 4 \\ -8 & -5 & 1 & 0 \\ 9 & 8 & 2 & 7 \\ -9 & -1 & -3 & 8 \\ -2 & 4 & -5 & 3 \end{bmatrix} + \begin{bmatrix} -5 & 4 & 8 & -3 \\ 8 & 4 & -5 & 3 \\ -5 & -9 & -4 & -8 \\ 7 & 5 & -2 & 0 \\ 7 & 5 & 4 & 1 \end{bmatrix} =$

Objectives: 1b

Matrix Subtraction

Matrices must be of the same order to perform subtraction. When subtracting matrices, change matrix subtraction into matrix addition by following the rule of "adding the opposite." To switch from matrix subtraction to matrix addition, make the "−" a "+" and change every element of the second matrix to its opposite. Do not change any elements of the first matrix. Then, follow the rule for matrix addition.

Example

$$\begin{bmatrix} 3 & 4 & -8 \\ -8 & 1 & 0 \end{bmatrix} - \begin{bmatrix} 7 & -2 & 9 \\ -4 & -9 & 3 \end{bmatrix} = \begin{bmatrix} 3 & 4 & -8 \\ -8 & 1 & 0 \end{bmatrix} + \begin{bmatrix} \mathbf{-7} & \mathbf{2} & \mathbf{-9} \\ \mathbf{4} & \mathbf{9} & \mathbf{-3} \end{bmatrix}$$

$$= \begin{bmatrix} -4 & 6 & -17 \\ -4 & 10 & -3 \end{bmatrix}$$

Example

$$\begin{bmatrix} 5 & 8 \\ -5 & 4 \\ 9 & -4 \end{bmatrix} - \begin{bmatrix} -5 & 2 \\ 3 & 8 \\ -2 & 0 \end{bmatrix} = \begin{bmatrix} 5 & 8 \\ -5 & 4 \\ 9 & -4 \end{bmatrix} + \begin{bmatrix} \mathbf{5} & \mathbf{-2} \\ \mathbf{-3} & \mathbf{-8} \\ \mathbf{2} & \mathbf{0} \end{bmatrix}$$

$$= \begin{bmatrix} 10 & 6 \\ -8 & -4 \\ 11 & -4 \end{bmatrix}$$

TIP: Variables can be used to name a matrix. For example, if

$M = \begin{bmatrix} 1 & 2 \\ 3 & 4 \end{bmatrix}$ and $N = \begin{bmatrix} 5 & 6 \\ 7 & 8 \end{bmatrix}$, then

$M + N = \begin{bmatrix} 6 & 8 \\ 10 & 12 \end{bmatrix}$ and $M - N = \begin{bmatrix} -4 & -4 \\ -4 & -4 \end{bmatrix}$.

Practice

Directions: For Numbers 1 through 4, subtract the matrices.

1. $\begin{bmatrix} 6 & 4 & -8 \\ -8 & 6 & -7 \\ 2 & 4 & 3 \\ 3 & -8 & -4 \end{bmatrix} - \begin{bmatrix} -4 & 6 & -2 \\ -1 & 0 & 8 \\ 8 & 4 & 8 \\ -3 & 4 & 0 \end{bmatrix} =$

2. $\begin{bmatrix} 2 & 8 & 7 & 4 \\ 9 & 8 & 4 & 2 \end{bmatrix} - \begin{bmatrix} 9 & -5 & 4 & 2 \\ -7 & 0 & 5 & 2 \end{bmatrix} =$

3. $\begin{bmatrix} -5 & 8 \\ 3 & 7 \\ 3 & 5 \\ -3 & -7 \\ 3 & 7 \end{bmatrix} - \begin{bmatrix} 6 & -4 \\ -8 & -1 \\ 8 & -1 \\ 8 & 4 \\ 8 & 4 \end{bmatrix} =$

4. $\begin{bmatrix} 2 & 8 & 7 & 4 \\ -8 & -5 & 1 & 0 \\ 9 & 8 & 2 & 7 \\ -9 & -1 & -3 & 8 \\ -2 & 4 & -5 & 3 \end{bmatrix} - \begin{bmatrix} -5 & 4 & 8 & -3 \\ 8 & 4 & -5 & 3 \\ -5 & -9 & -4 & -8 \\ 7 & 5 & -2 & 0 \\ 7 & 5 & 4 & 1 \end{bmatrix} =$

Objectives: 1b

Scalar Multiplication

A scalar in matrix algebra is the equivalent to a constant (any real number) in basic algebra. Therefore, **scalar multiplication** means multiplying a matrix by a real number. The result is a matrix of the same order as the original, formed by multiplying each element of the original by the scalar.

Example

$$6\begin{bmatrix} 3 & -8 & 7 \\ 8 & 4 & -2 \\ -1 & 5 & 0 \end{bmatrix} = \begin{bmatrix} \mathbf{6} \bullet 3 & \mathbf{6} \bullet (-8) & \mathbf{6} \bullet 7 \\ \mathbf{6} \bullet 8 & \mathbf{6} \bullet 4 & \mathbf{6} \bullet (-2) \\ \mathbf{6} \bullet (-1) & \mathbf{6} \bullet 5 & \mathbf{6} \bullet 0 \end{bmatrix}$$

$$= \begin{bmatrix} 18 & -48 & 42 \\ 48 & 24 & -12 \\ -6 & 30 & 0 \end{bmatrix}$$

Example

$$-2\begin{bmatrix} 5 & 8 \\ -2 & -7 \\ -3 & 1 \\ -8 & 4 \\ 6 & -5 \\ 2 & 0 \end{bmatrix} = \begin{bmatrix} \mathbf{-2} \bullet 5 & \mathbf{-2} \bullet 8 \\ \mathbf{-2} \bullet (-2) & \mathbf{-2} \bullet (-7) \\ \mathbf{-2} \bullet (-3) & \mathbf{-2} \bullet 1 \\ \mathbf{-2} \bullet (-8) & \mathbf{-2} \bullet 4 \\ \mathbf{-2} \bullet 6 & \mathbf{-2} \bullet (-5) \\ \mathbf{-2} \bullet 2 & \mathbf{-2} \bullet 0 \end{bmatrix}$$

$$= \begin{bmatrix} -10 & -16 \\ 4 & 14 \\ 6 & -2 \\ 16 & -8 \\ -12 & 10 \\ -4 & 0 \end{bmatrix}$$

TIP: If $P = \begin{bmatrix} 1 & 2 \\ 3 & 4 \end{bmatrix} P$, then $3P = \begin{bmatrix} 3 & 6 \\ 9 & 12 \end{bmatrix}$.

Practice

Directions: For Numbers 1 through 4, multiply to find the scalar product.

1. $5\begin{bmatrix} 8 & -5 & 3 & -4 & 9 \\ -2 & 5 & -7 & -4 & 0 \end{bmatrix} =$

2. $-7\begin{bmatrix} 5 & -7 & 6 & 3 & -4 & -8 \\ 4 & -5 & 2 & -1 & 1 & 2 \\ 3 & -2 & 4 & -8 & -2 & -3 \\ 5 & -4 & -8 & 10 & -14 & 2 \end{bmatrix} =$

3. $-9\begin{bmatrix} 2 & -4 & -3 \\ 2 & 0 & 4 \\ 1 & -8 & -9 \\ 0 & -8 & -4 \\ -8 & -4 & 2 \\ -1 & 4 & 8 \end{bmatrix} =$

4. $0\begin{bmatrix} 5 & 6 & 4 \\ 1 & -8 & -4 \\ 257 & 368 & -485 \end{bmatrix} =$

TIP: The matrix formed in Number 4 is called the **zero matrix**. Any matrix in which all the elements are zero is called a zero matrix.

Objectives: 1b

Applications of Matrices

Matrices can be useful for organizing numbers in real-world situations.

Example

Tyler, Emily, Libby, and Daniel each made $7 an hour working at the car wash during summer vacation. The following matrix shows the number of hours each worked in June, July, and August.

Hours Worked

	Tyler	Emily	Libby	Daniel
June	116	106	98	125
July	124	108	110	85
August	96	99	93	101

Represent in a matrix the amount of money each earned in June, July, and August. (Multiply the matrix above by 7.)

$$7\begin{bmatrix} 116 & 106 & 98 & 125 \\ 124 & 108 & 110 & 85 \\ 96 & 99 & 93 & 101 \end{bmatrix} = \begin{bmatrix} 812 & 742 & 686 & 875 \\ 868 & 756 & 770 & 595 \\ 672 & 693 & 651 & 707 \end{bmatrix}$$

The following matrix shows the amounts of money that Tyler, Emily, Libby, and Daniel earned in June, July, and August.

Money Earned (in dollars)

	Tyler	Emily	Libby	Daniel
June	812	742	686	875
July	868	756	770	595
August	672	693	651	707

Practice

Directions: Use the following information to answer Numbers 1 through 3.

A sporting-goods store sells football jerseys in three different colors and four different sizes. The store makes $25 for each jersey it sells. The numbers of jerseys sold are represented in the following matrices.

Jerseys Sold in October

	S	M	L	XL
Burgundy	36	39	72	62
Gold	41	25	65	40
White	17	30	47	58

Jerseys Sold in November

	S	M	L	XL
Burgundy	35	51	56	74
Gold	36	38	47	55
White	24	22	40	63

1. Represent in a matrix the number of each size and color jersey sold in October and November combined.

2. Represent in a matrix the amount of money the store made selling each size and color jersey in October.

3. How much money did the store make selling jerseys for the entire month of November?

SATP Practice begins on the following page.

1. Simplify the following expression.

$$-x^2 + 2x + 3x^2 + 4x - 4y^2 + 16y$$

A $2x^2 + 6x - 4y^2 + 16y$

B $20x^2xy^2y$

C $20x^2y^2 + 20xy$

D $8x^2x + 12y^2y$

---

2. Add: $\begin{bmatrix} 24 & -9 \\ -20 & 28 \\ 88 & 10 \end{bmatrix} + \begin{bmatrix} -1 & -18 \\ 8 & 40 \\ -19 & -99 \end{bmatrix}$

F $\begin{bmatrix} 25 & 27 \\ 28 & 68 \\ 107 & 109 \end{bmatrix}$

H $\begin{bmatrix} 25 & -9 \\ -28 & 68 \\ 107 & 109 \end{bmatrix}$

G $\begin{bmatrix} 23 & 27 \\ -28 & 68 \\ 67 & -89 \end{bmatrix}$

J $\begin{bmatrix} 23 & -27 \\ -12 & 68 \\ 69 & -89 \end{bmatrix}$

---

3. Simplify the following expression.

$$8s^2 + 9r^2 + 18 - 6r - 12 + 9s^2$$

A $17s^2 + 3r^2 + 6$

B $17s^2 + 9r^2 - 6r + 30$

C $17s^2 + 9r^2 - 6r + 6$

D $17s^2 + 9r^2 + 18 - 6r^2 - 12 + 9s^2$

---

4. **Subtract:** $\begin{bmatrix} 3 & -6 & 4 & -2 \\ 9 & -3 & 7 & -5 \end{bmatrix} - \begin{bmatrix} 14 & -8 & 0 & 6 \\ -3 & -22 & 4 & 9 \end{bmatrix}$

F $\begin{bmatrix} 11 & -2 & 4 & -4 \\ 6 & -19 & 11 & 14 \end{bmatrix}$

G $\begin{bmatrix} 17 & -14 & 4 & 4 \\ 6 & -25 & 10 & 4 \end{bmatrix}$

H $\begin{bmatrix} -3 & -6 & 4 & -16 \\ 0 & -7 & 29 & -2 \end{bmatrix}$

J $\begin{bmatrix} -11 & 2 & 4 & -8 \\ 12 & 19 & 3 & -14 \end{bmatrix}$

---

5. **Multiply:** $4\begin{bmatrix} -3 & -5 & -6 \\ 4 & 10 & -8 \\ 2 & 5 & 6 \end{bmatrix}$

A $\begin{bmatrix} 1 & -1 & -2 \\ 0 & 14 & -4 \\ 6 & 9 & 10 \end{bmatrix}$

B $\begin{bmatrix} -12 & -20 & -24 \\ 16 & 40 & -32 \\ 8 & 20 & 24 \end{bmatrix}$

C $\begin{bmatrix} 12 & 20 & 24 \\ 16 & 40 & 32 \\ 8 & 20 & 24 \end{bmatrix}$

D $\begin{bmatrix} 7 & 9 & 10 \\ 0 & -6 & 12 \\ 2 & -1 & -2 \end{bmatrix}$

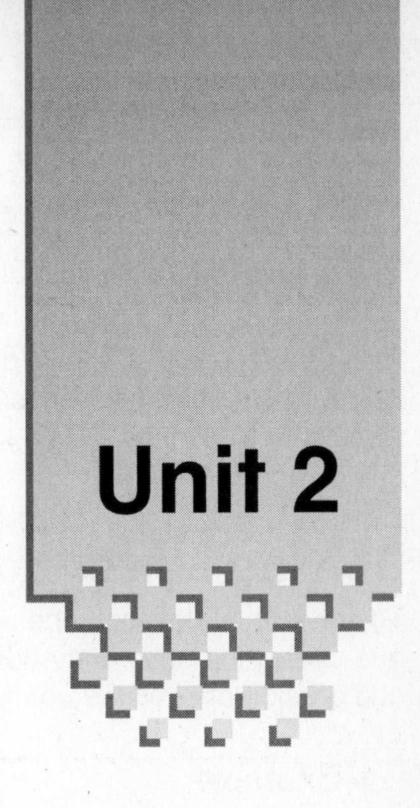

Algebra

Cash registers have been programmed with rules that automatically figure the sales tax that should be charged on a purchase. Chemists use systems of linear equations to precisely mix solutions. Physicists use a quadratic equation to determine the maximum height that a ball can reach when thrown into the air at some initial velocity.

In this unit, you will solve and graph linear, absolute value, and quadratic equations. You will represent a linear equation in different ways, interpret the meaning of the slope and intercepts of a linear equation and write linear equations based on a situation. You will also learn how to identify if a relationship is a function. Finally, you will perform operations on and solve polynomials.

In This Unit

Lesson 2: Equations and Inequalities in One Variable

In this lesson, you will solve different types of equations and inequalities in one variable. You will also solve problem situations by writing equations and inequalities and then solving them.

Solving Linear Equations

To solve an equation in one variable, use inverse operations to isolate the variable on one side of the equation. Addition and subtraction are inverse operations. Multiplication and division are inverse operations.

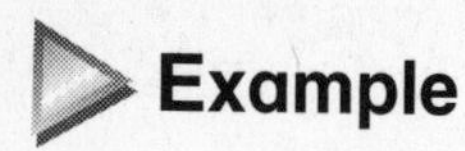

Example

Solve the following equation for n.

$$2{,}651 + 2n = 965 - 4n$$

Use inverse operations to isolate the variable.

$2{,}651 + 2n = 965 - 4n$ (Add $4n$ to both sides.)

$2{,}651 + 6n = 965$ (Subtract 2,651 from both sides.)

$6n = -1{,}686$ (Divide both sides by 6.)

$n = -281$

Check your solution by substituting −281 for n in the original equation.

$$2{,}651 + 2n = 965 - 4n$$

$$2{,}651 + 2(\mathbf{-281}) = 965 - 4(\mathbf{-281})$$

$$2{,}651 - 562 = 965 + 1{,}124$$

$$2{,}089 = 2{,}089$$

Since the substitution makes the equation true, the solution is $n = -281$.

Objectives: 2a

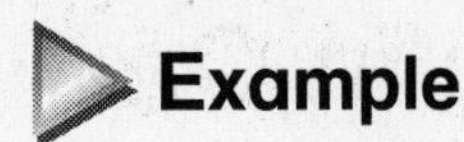

Example

Solve the following equation for *x*.

$$\frac{2}{3}x - \frac{1}{4} = \frac{3}{8}$$

In an equation like this, it may be helpful to multiply each side by a constant before using inverse operations to isolate the variable.

$$\frac{2}{3}x - \frac{1}{4} = \frac{3}{8}$$ (Multiply both sides by the LCD of the fractions, 24.)

$$24\left(\frac{2}{3}x - \frac{1}{4}\right) = 24\left(\frac{3}{8}\right)$$ (Simplify.)

$$16x - 6 = 9$$ (Add 6 to both sides.)

$$16x = 15$$ (Divide both sides by 16.)

$$x = \frac{15}{16}$$

Check your solution.

$$\frac{2}{3}x - \frac{1}{4} = \frac{3}{8}$$

$$\frac{2}{3}\left(\mathbf{\frac{15}{16}}\right) - \frac{1}{4} = \frac{3}{8}$$

$$\frac{5}{8} - \frac{1}{4} = \frac{3}{8}$$

$$\frac{5}{8} - \frac{2}{8} = \frac{3}{8}$$

$$\frac{3}{8} = \frac{3}{8}$$

Since the substitution makes the equation true, the solution is $x = \frac{15}{16}$.

Practice

Directions: For Numbers 1 through 12, solve each equation and check your solution.

1. $5y + 17 = 97$

2. $2h + 15.6 = -46.8$

3. $\frac{x}{8} + 8.3 = -4.8$

4. $\frac{2}{3}d - \frac{5}{6} = \frac{11}{12}$

5. $\frac{x}{7} - 8 = -12$

6. $31.82 - 2y = -4.5y + 3.92$

7. $-\frac{3}{5}b - \frac{1}{10} = \frac{7}{20} - \frac{7}{10}b$

8. $4(3z - 5) = -8$

9. $\frac{v}{3} + \frac{1}{4} = \frac{5}{12}$

10. $7w - 3(6 + 2w) = 3(w - 8)$

11. $3a + 8 - 5a = -7(a + 1)$

12. $3(4 - 2d) - 6 = 2(5d - 5)$

Objectives: 2a

Writing and Solving Linear Equations

When you solve application problems, you can translate the problem into an algebraic equation. Then, you can solve for the unknown variable to find the answer to the problem.

Example

Marge bought boxes of wood flooring for her dining room floor. Each box contains 15 pieces of wood flooring. She used 243 pieces of wood flooring and had 12 pieces leftover. How many boxes of wood flooring did Marge buy?

You can write the following equation to represent this situation, where b is the number of boxes of wood flooring Marge bought.

$$15b - 12 = 243$$

Solve the equation for b.

$15b - 12 = 243$ (Add 12 to both sides.)

$15b = 255$ (Divide both sides by 15.)

$b = 17$

Marge bought 17 boxes of wood flooring.

Example

Christine spent \$95 at a furniture store. She bought a bookshelf for \$79 and some bookends for \$4 each. How many bookends did Christine buy?

You can write the following equation to represent this situation, where b is the number of bookends Christine bought.

$$4b + 79 = 95$$

Solve the equation for b.

$4b + 79 = 95$ (Subtract 79 from both sides.)

$4b = 16$ (Divide both sides by 4.)

$b = 4$

Christine bought 4 bookends.

Practice

Directions: For Numbers 1 through 6, write an equation to represent each application problem. Then, solve the equation to find the answer to the problem.

1. Jessica spent a total of $627.83 at the High Street Antique Mall in Jackson. She bought a desk for $185.71 and 2 identical chairs. How much did each chair, *c*, cost?

2. Alliyah has 3 times as many hair ties as Marcy. Together, they have a total of 56 hair ties. How many hair ties, *h*, does Marcy have?

3. Rico had 19 golf balls. He then bought some containers of golf balls at Sport-Mart. Each container contained 3 golf balls. Rico increased the number of golf balls he owns to a total of 58 golf balls. How many containers of golf balls, *c*, did Rico buy?

4. At Charlie's Sub Shop, a sub costs $5.95. Extra condiments are available for $0.25 each. If Maria bought a sub for $7.20, how many extra condiments, *c*, did she order?

5. Alyssa bought a bag of peanuts. She ate 57 peanuts and then divided the remaining peanuts equally among 4 friends. Each person received 21 peanuts. How many peanuts, *p*, were in the bag?

6. Marcus rented a boat for the weekend. The rental company charged him $44.75 per hour, plus the cost of gas. If the cost of gas was $18.60 and Marcus paid a total of $197.60 for the boat rental, how many hours, *h*, did he have the boat?

Objectives: 2a

Solving Linear Inequalities

To solve inequalities ($>$, $<$, $\geq$, or $\leq$), follow the same steps that apply to equations (from page 18). If you multiply or divide by a negative number, switch the sign to the opposite direction.

Example

Solve for x: $\frac{x}{5} + 6 > 15$ (Subtract 6 from both sides.)

$\frac{x}{5} > 9$ (Multiply both sides by 5.)

$x > 45$

Check your solution by substituting any value that satisfies your answer into the original inequality and simplifying.

$$\frac{x}{5} + 6 > 15$$

$$\frac{\mathbf{48}}{5} + 6 > 15$$

$$9.6 + 6 > 15$$

$$15.6 > 15$$

Since the substitution makes the inequality true, the solution is $x > 45$.

Example

Solve for x: $-3x - 3 \leq 4x + 39$ (Add $-4x$ and 3 to both sides.)

$-7x \leq 42$ (Divide both sides by -7.)

$x \geq -6$ (Switch the directions of the sign since you divided by a negative number.)

Check your solution by substituting any value that satisfies your answer into the original inequality and simplifying.

$$-3x - 3 \leq 4x + 39$$

$$-3(\mathbf{-3}) - 3 \leq 4(\mathbf{-3}) + 39$$

$$9 - 3 \leq -12 + 39$$

$$6 \leq 27$$

Since the substitution makes the inequality true, the solution is $x \geq -6$.

Practice

Directions: For Numbers 1 through 12, solve the inequality and check your solution.

1. $7x > 8 + 9x$

2. $3(y - 2) < 12$

3. $\frac{1}{2}x + 4 \geq 23$

4. $5(p + 2) + 4(p - 3) < 24 - 7p$

5. $2(5 - 3x) \leq 22$

6. $22 + 11b \geq b + 28$

7. $36.4 + 1.2a \geq 44.44$

8. $\frac{2}{3}z - \frac{1}{6} \leq \frac{1}{2} - \frac{1}{6}z$

9. $-8(c - 2) > 40$

10. $4(2s + 3) > 5(s - 6)$

11. $-2(4 - 7t) < -6(3t + 4)$

12. $6(2x - 8) + 3(x + 5) \leq 2$

Graphing Linear Inequalities

Unlike equations in one variable, there are an infinite number of solutions to most inequalities in one variable. The graph of an inequality shows an open or a closed dot on a number line and shading on one side of the dot. There is an open dot if the sign from the solution is either $<$ or $>$; there is a closed dot if the sign from the solution is either $\leq$ or $\geq$. The part of the number line that is shaded will show the numbers that can be substituted for the variable in the inequality to make the inequality true.

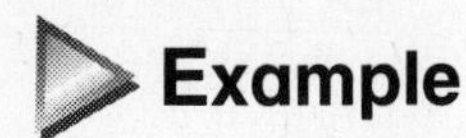

Example

Graph the inequality: $-2x + 8 \leq 3x + 38$

Before you can graph the inequality, you must solve it for x.

$-2x + 8 \leq 3x + 38$ (Add -8 and $-3x$ to both sides.)

$-5x \leq 30$ (Divide both sides by -5.)

$x \geq -6$ (Switch the direction of the sign since you divided by a negative number.)

Here is the graph of the inequality.

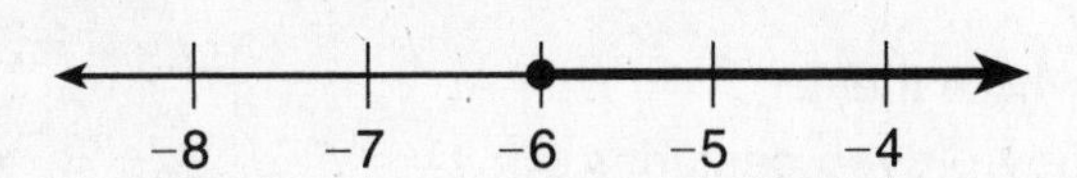

Since -6 and any number greater than -6 can be substituted for x in the inequality $-2x + 8 \leq 3x + 38$ to make it true, the -6 has a closed dot and the number line to the right of -6 is shaded.

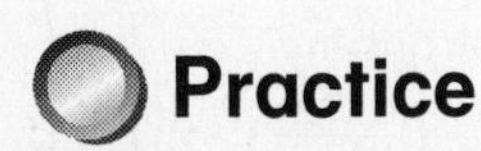

Practice

Directions: For Numbers 1 through 6, solve each inequality and check your solution. Then, graph the inequality.

1. $7s + 11 > 4s - 31$

2. $6 - 5y + 15 \leq 2y - y$

3. $2 - 3(t + 5) \geq 6(2t - 8)$

4. $-4.2g + 6.04 < -5.56 + 7.4g$

5. $-\frac{1}{4}w + 1\frac{1}{3} \geq \frac{1}{3}\left(w + \frac{1}{2}\right)$

6. $-2(5 - 6t) < -2(10t + 13)$

People in Math

For all of the attention we pay to our calendars, do we ever think about where they came from? Or what a major role they played centuries ago?

The story of Chinese mathematician Zu Chongzhi has enough secrets and plots to be a blockbuster movie. But he wasn't a spy or an undercover agent. He came up with a new calendar!

Zu Chongzhi
(429–501)

Zu Chongzhi was born into a very influential family in 429 CE. For hundreds of years, the Zu family name had been associated with powerful court officials and brilliant astronomers. Zu's father wanted to make sure that his son knew all about astronomy, science, and mathematics.

When he was old enough, Zu was appointed to a high position in the court of Emperor Xiao-wu. Zu began working on a new calendar for the monarch. This was particularly important, because people in ancient China believed that calendars provided a link from the emperor to the heavens.

Zu estimated the year's length nearly perfectly. (He was only 50 seconds off.) His calendar was far more accurate than any other. But Zu had an enemy in the emperor's court. Tai Faxin complained that Zu's calendar went against religious beliefs. Zu argued back that calendars shouldn't be based upon "spirits or ghosts," but upon scientific calculations.

The emperor died before he could introduce Zu's calendar to the people of China. The new emperor listened to Tai Faxin and refused to use Zu's calendar. In spite of this setback, Zu left a successful legacy. In addition to his work with calendars, he was one of the first mathematicians to calculate pi to six decimal places.

Objectives: 2a

Writing and Solving Linear Inequalities

Sometimes you will have to write an inequality to solve an application problem. The steps that apply to writing equations also apply to writing inequalities. Here are a few words that usually indicate an inequality: *at least*, *more than*, *less than*, *no more than*, *greater than*, *no less than*, *minimum*, *maximum*.

Example

Kenny needs more than 120 hours of credit to graduate from college. He has already earned 87 hours of credit. Each class he has left to take will earn him 3 hours of credit. What is the minimum number of classes that Kenny can take to graduate?

You can write the following inequality to represent this situation, where c is the number of classes Kenny has left to take.

$3c + 87 > 120$ (Subtract 87 from both sides.)

$3c > 33$ (Divide both sides by 3.)

$c > 11$

Kenny must take at least 12 classes to graduate.

Example

Carter saw some white-tailed deer while hiking through the Great River Road State Park on Monday. On Tuesday, he saw twice as many white-tailed deer as he saw on Monday. If Carter saw no more than 36 white-tailed deer, what is the largest number of white-tailed deer he saw each day?

You can write the following inequality to represent this situation, where d is the number of white-tailed deer Carter saw on Monday.

$d + 2d \leq 36$ (Simplify.)

$3d \leq 36$ (Divide both sides by 3.)

$d \leq 12$

$2d \leq 24$

Carter saw a maximum of 12 white-tailed deer on Monday and a maximum of 24 white-tailed deer on Tuesday.

Practice

Directions: For Numbers 1 through 6, write an inequality to represent each application problem. Then, solve the inequality to find the answer to the problem.

1. At the Pizza Palace, a large pizza costs $12.89. Extra toppings are available for $1.25 each. If Elijah paid for his pizza with a $20 bill, what is the most extra toppings, *t*, he could have ordered?

2. Miss Baxter wants to divide the students in her knitting class into groups of no more than 4 students. There are 42 students in the class, and 5 students are absent. What is the least number of groups, *g*, into which the students can be divided?

3. Elgin rides his pony more than 85 minutes each week. Elgin rode his pony a total of 29 minutes from Monday through Friday. He also rode his pony an equal amount of time on Saturday and Sunday. What is the minimum number of minutes, *m*, Elgin rode on Saturday?

4. Madison had a garage sale and priced all her jewelry at either $0.90 or $1.25. Ariana spent as much of her $10 at the garage sale as she could. She bought 2 pieces of jewelry that were $1.25 and she bought as many $0.90 pieces as she could with the remaining money. What was the maximum number of $0.90-pieces of jewelry, *j*, that Ariana could have bought?

5. Evan earns $8 per hour and $4 per sale. Evan works an 8-hour shift and wants to make at least $100 during his shift. How many sales, *s*, must Evan make to earn at least $100 during his shift?

6. Admission to Rapids on the Reservoir is $21.39 for adults and $18.18 for children. Maggie has $100 and wants to take as many of her children as she can with her to the park. How many of Maggie's children, *c*, can go with her to the park?

Objectives: 2b

Solving Absolute Value Equations

Remember that the absolute value of a number is defined as its distance from zero on a number line, and is always positive or zero ($|x| \geq 0$). If $|x| = 5$, then the solutions are $x = 5$ and $x = -5$, because both 5 and −5 are five units from zero on the number line. The same thought process is used when you solve multi-step absolute value equations. To solve an absolute value equation, follow these steps:

Step 1: **Isolate the absolute value term on one side of the equal sign.**

Step 2: **Write two different equations separated by "or" so that:**

1) **the expression inside the absolute value symbol equals the number on the right side of the equal sign.**
2) **the expression inside the absolute value symbol equals the opposite of the number on the right side of the equal sign.**

Step 3: **Solve each equation and check each solution.**

Example

Solve the following equation for x.

$$|2x - 7| = 5$$

Because the absolute value term is already isolated on the left side of the equation, you can set up and solve two equations.

$2x - 7 = 5$	or	$2x - 7 = -5$	(Add 7 to both sides.)
$2x = 12$		$2x = 2$	(Divide both sides by 2.)
$x = 6$		$x = 1$	

Check your solutions by substituting your answers into the original equation and simplifying.

$\lvert 2(\mathbf{6}) - 7\rvert = 5$	and	$\lvert 2(\mathbf{1}) - 7\rvert = 5$
$\lvert 12 - 7\rvert = 5$		$\lvert 2 - 7\rvert = 5$
$\lvert 5\rvert = 5$		$\lvert -5\rvert = 5$
$5 = 5$		$5 = 5$

Since the substitutions make both equations true, the solutions are $x = 6$ and $x = 1$.

Example

Solve the following equation for y.

$|5y + 10| - 8 = 18$

Use inverse operations to isolate the absolute value term on the left side of the equation.

$|5y + 10| - 8 = 18$ (Add 8 to both sides.)

$|5y + 10| = 26$

Set up and solve two equations.

$5y + 10 = 26$ or $5y + 10 = -26$ (Subtract 10 from both sides.)

$5y = 16$ $5y = -36$ (Divide both sides by 5.)

$y = \frac{16}{5}$ $y = -\frac{36}{5}$

Check your solutions by substituting your answers into the original equations and simplifying.

$\left|5\left(\frac{16}{5}\right) + 10\right| - 8 = 18$ and $\left|5\left(-\frac{36}{5}\right) + 10\right| - 8 = 18$

$|26| - 8 = 18$ $|-26| - 8 = 18$

$26 - 8 = 18$ $26 - 8 = 18$

$26 = 26$ $26 = 26$

Since the substitutions make the equations true, the solutions are $y = \frac{16}{5}$ and $y = -\frac{36}{5}$.

Example

Solve the following equation for a.

$|4a - 7| + 12 = 1$

Use inverse operations to isolate the absolute value term on the left side of the equation.

$|4a - 7| + 12 = 1$ (Subtract 12 from both sides.)

$|4a - 7| = -11$

Notice that the absolute value is equal to a negative number. Because an absolute value must equal a positive number or zero, there is no solution.

Practice

Directions: For Numbers 1 through 6, solve each absolute value equation and check your solutions.

1. $|2 - p| = 6$

2. $|5d - 4| + 2 = 13$

3. $|11x - 7| + 6 = 2$

4. $|3t - 6| = 9$

5. $|7s + 3| - 6 = -2$

6. $4|y| - 5 = 11$

Solving Absolute Value Inequalities

The process for solving absolute value inequalities includes solving inequalities. To solve an absolute value inequality, follow these steps:

Step 1: **Isolate the absolute value term on one side of the inequality sign.**

Step 2: **Write two different inequalities separated by "or" if $\geq$ or $>$ is used and separated by "and" if $\leq$ or $<$ is used.**

Step 3: **Write the first inequality by dropping the absolute value symbol from the original inequality.**

Step 4: **Write the second inequality by dropping the absolute value symbol, reversing the inequality sign, and taking the opposite of the number on the right side of the original inequality.**

Step 5: **Solve each inequality and check each solution.**

Example

Solve the following inequality for x.

$|2x - 8| < 4$

Because the absolute value symbol is already isolated on the left, write and solve two inequalities. The inequality symbol used is $<$, so separate the inequalities with "and." Remember to reverse the inequality symbol on the second inequality.

$2x - 8 < 4$	and	$2x - 8 > -4$	(Add 8 to both sides.)
$2x < 12$	and	$2x > 4$	(Divide both sides by 2.)
$x < 6$	and	$x > 2$	

Check your solutions.

$|2(\mathbf{5}) - 8| < 4$	and	$|2(\mathbf{3}) - 8| < 4$
$|10 - 8| < 4$		$|6 - 8| < 4$
$|2| < 4$		$|-2| < 4$
$2 < 4$		$2 < 4$

Since the substitutions make the inequalities true, the solution is $x < 6$ and $x > 2$, which can also be written as $2 < x < 6$.

Objectives: 2b

Example

Solve the following inequality for y.

$|3y - 4| - 8 \geq 12$

Use inverse operations to isolate the absolute value term on the left side of the inequality.

$|3y - 4| - 8 \geq 12$ (Add 8 to both sides.)

$|3y - 4| \geq 20$

Set up and solve two inequalities. The inequality symbol used is $\geq$, so separate the inequalities with "or." Remember to reverse the inequality symbol on the second inequality.

$3y - 4 \geq 20$ or $3y - 4 \leq -20$ (Add 4 to both sides.)

$3y \geq 24$ or $3y \leq -16$ (Divide both sides by 3.)

$y \geq 8$ or $y \leq -\frac{16}{3}$

Example

Solve the following inequality for a.

$|2a + 18| + 10 \leq 7$

Use inverse operations to isolate the absolute value term on the left side of the inequality.

$|2a + 18| + 10 \leq 7$ (Subtract 10 from both sides.)

$|2a + 18| \leq -3$

Notice that the absolute value is less than or equal to a negative number. Because an absolute value must equal a positive number or zero, there is no solution.

Practice

Directions: For Numbers 1 through 6, solve each absolute value inequality and check your solution.

1. $|14 - 2w| \leq 6$

2. $|2c - 8| + 2 > 9$

3. $|3b - 8| - 6 < 2$

4. $|4t + 1| \geq 7$

5. $|12r + 8| \leq -5$

6. $2|v| - 3 < 11$

Graphing Absolute Value Inequalities

Absolute value inequalities have either an infinite number of solutions or no solution. There are three types of graphs of absolute value inequalities.

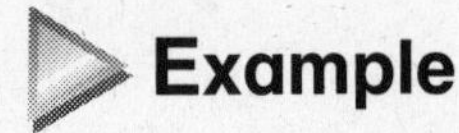

Example

Graph the absolute value inequality: $|2x - 8| < 4$

From page 32, the solution to the absolute value inequality $|2x - 8| < 4$ is $2 < x < 6$. Here is the graph of the inequality.

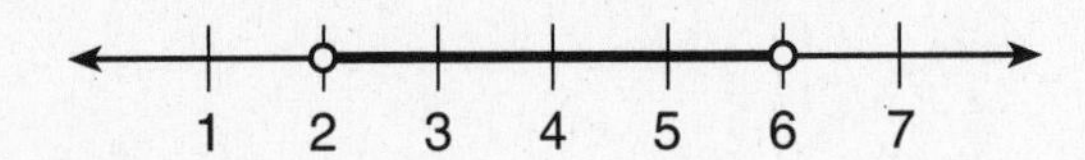

Because solutions to the inequality have to be greater than 2 and less than 6, the range between 2 and 6 is shaded and an open dot is used.

Example

Graph the absolute value inequality: $|3y - 4| - 8 \geq 12$

From page 33, the solution to the absolute value inequality $|3y - 4| - 8 \geq 12$ is $y \geq 8$ or $y \leq -\frac{16}{3}$. Here is the graph of the inequality.

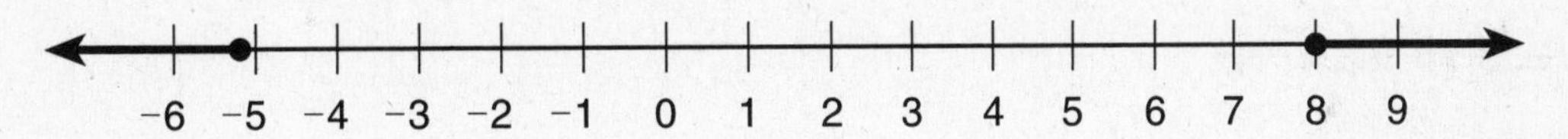

Because solutions to the inequality have to be greater than or equal to 8 or less than or equal to $-5\frac{1}{3}$, the ranges to the left of $-5\frac{1}{3}$ and to the right of 8 are shaded and a closed dot is used.

Example

Graph the absolute value inequality: $|2a + 18| + 10 \leq 7$

From page 33, there is no solution to the absolute value inequality $|2a + 18| + 10 \leq 7$. There is no graph of the inequality.

Practice

Directions: For Numbers 1 through 6, solve and then graph each absolute value inequality. Then, check your solution.

1. $|5 - 2w| \leq 6$

2. $|4r + 6| \leq -4$

3. $|b - 6| - 9 > -1$

4. $3|v| - 2 < 13$

5. $|3c - 3| + 3 < 15$

6. $|5t + 13| \geq 12$

SATP Practice begins on the following page.

1. Tom bought several tickets to the Harper and Morgan Professional Rodeo for his family. Tickets were \$6.25 each. Tom gave the cashier a \$50 bill and received \$18.75 in change. Which of the following equations could be used to find the number of tickets, *n*, Tom bought?

A $6.25n + 18.75 = 50.00$

B $6.25n - 18.75 = 50.00$

C $6.25n - 50.00 = 18.75$

D $6.25n + 50.00 = 18.75$

---

2. What is the solution to the following inequality?

$$-5z - 8 < -2.5$$

F $z > 1.1$

G $z < 1.1$

H $z > -1.1$

J $z < -1.1$

---

3. Mariah has \$80. She wants to buy a \$15 DVD and as many \$10 CDs as she can. Which phrase BEST describes the number of CDs Mariah can buy?

A Less than 6

B More than 6

C At most 6

D At least 6

---

4. What is the solution to the following equation?

$$|-2x - 4| - 3 = 9$$

F $x = -4$ and $x = 8$

G $x = -8$ and $x = 4$

H $x = -12$ and $x = 6$

J $x = -6$ and $x = 12$

---

5. **What is the solution to the following equation?**

$$18n + 28 = -20 + 2n$$

A $n = -3$

B $n = -\frac{8}{3}$

C $n = \frac{1}{2}$

D $n = \frac{2}{5}$

---

6. **Tony has a collection of dimes and quarters. He has 325 coins in his collection for a total of $47.80. Which equation could be used to find the number of dimes, *d*, in his collection?**

F $325(0.25)d + 325(0.10)d = 478$

G $0.10d + 0.25(325 - d) = 47.80$

H $0.10d + 325(0.25d) = 47.80$

J $0.35d + 325 = 4{,}780$

---

7. **What is the solution to the following inequality?**

$$|b + 6| + 10 \leq 15$$

A $-11 \leq b \leq -1$

B $-11 \leq b \leq 11$

C $-31 \leq b \leq 19$

D $-31 \leq b \leq 31$

---

8. **José has $17. He ordered large french fries for $1.59 and a large soda for $1.99. He wants to order as many $1.49 hamburgers as he can with the rest of his money. What is the largest number of hamburgers that José can order?**

F 6

G 7

H 8

J 9

---

9. **What is the solution to the following inequality?**

$$6 - 7x \geq -5x + 18$$

A $x \geq -6$

B $x \geq -2$

C $x \leq -6$

D $x \leq -2$

---

10. **What is the solution to the following equation?**

$$-2(y + 9) = 14$$

F $y = 16$

G $y = 2$

H $y = -2$

J $y = -16$

---

11. **What is the solution to the following inequality?**

$$-\frac{5}{2}x + 11 \leq \frac{7}{2}x - 13$$

A $x \geq 4$

B $x \leq 4$

C $x \geq -4$

D $x \leq -4$

---

12. **What is the solution to the following inequality?**

$$4y + \frac{7}{4} \geq y + \frac{3}{4}$$

F $y \leq \frac{1}{3}$

G $y \geq \frac{1}{3}$

H $y \leq -\frac{1}{3}$

J $y \geq -\frac{1}{3}$

Lesson 3: Relations and Functions

One of the most common uses of algebra is to find out how a change in a value of one quantity affects the value of another quantity. In this lesson, you will review the basic terminology and components of relations and functions.

Terminology

The variable you start with is called the **domain** or the input value. The variable whose value you are looking for is called the **range** or the output value. A relationship between a domain and its range is called a **relation**. A **function** is a special relation in which each value of the domain is matched with exactly one value of the range. The variable that represents the domain values is also called the **independent variable**. Its value can be any of the values in the domain. The variable that represents the range values is also called the **dependent variable**. Its value is determined by the value of the independent variable.

Example

Identify what the independent and dependent variables are and what they represent for the following functional relationship. Then, determine the domain and range.

The perimeter of a square is found by multiplying the square's side length by 4. The function is represented by the equation.

$$P = 4s$$

The independent variable, s, represents the side length of the square.

The dependent variable, P, represents the perimeter of the square.

The domain is determined by the values of the independent variable. Since the independent variable represents the length of a segment, it must be a positive real number. The domain is the set of positive real numbers.

The range is determined by the values of the independent variable. In this example, each value of the independent variable is multiplied by 4. So, if each positive real number is multiplied by 4, you get a positive real number. The range is also the set of positive real numbers.

You say, "The perimeter of a square is a function of its side length."

Objectives: 2c, 2d

A relation may be given in the form of a set of ordered pairs that matches each domain value with its corresponding range value. If there are no specific variables associated with the relation, x is generally used to represent the domain values and y is used to represent the range values. Then, the ordered pairs can be represented as (x, y). To determine if a relation in the form of ordered pairs represents a functional relationship, make sure that each domain value is matched with exactly one range value.

Example

The following set of ordered pairs is a relation.

$\{(3, 4), (5, 6), (3, 9), (5, 8)\}$

What are the domain and the range of this relation? If you draw a table and put in the ordered pairs, the values of the domain and range are easier to spot. To find the domain, look at all the x-coordinates; to find the range, look at all the y-coordinates. When writing the domain and range, arrange the values from least to greatest and omit values that appear more than once.

x	y
3	4
5	6
3	9
5	8

domain {3, 5}

range {4, 6, 8, 9}

The following graph shows this relation. Notice that there is no attempt to make a line, curve, or any connections at all. Relations do not always produce lines, curves, or other figures. Sometimes they are merely random points on a graph.

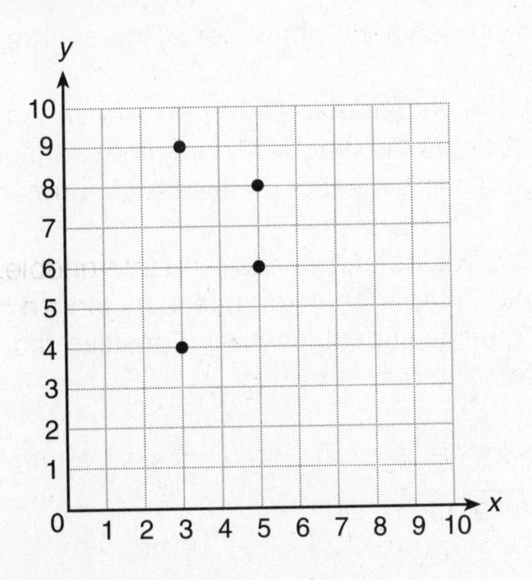

Example

Is the relation from the previous page also a function?

{(3, 4), (5, 6), (3, 9), (5, 8)}

Are there any points that have the same *x*-coordinates? Yes. The points (**3**, 4) and (**3**, 9) have the same *x*-coordinate. The points (**5**, 6) and (**5**, 8) also have the same *x*-coordinate.

Therefore, the relation is not a function.

Example

The following relation is a function.

{(1, 2), (2, 4), (3, 6), (4, 8)}

Notice that all of the *x*-coordinates are different. The following table shows the values of the domain and the range.

x	*y*
1	2
2	4
3	6
4	8

domain {1, 2, 3, 4}

range {2, 4, 6, 8}

The following graph shows this function. You can see that there is exactly one point plotted for each value in the domain.

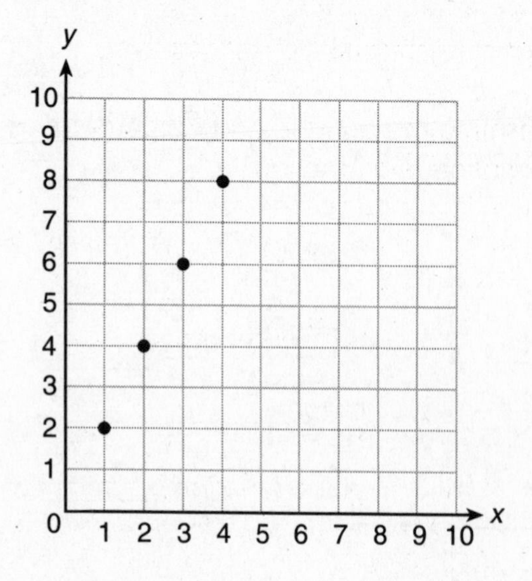

Objectives: 2c, 2d **DOK 2**

Practice

Directions: For Numbers 1 and 2, identify what the independent and dependent variables are and what they represent for each of the functional relationships. Then, determine the possible domain and range.

1. The cost of a pizza at The Pizza Shop is $13.59 plus $1.20 for each topping. The function is represented by the equation:

   $c = 13.59 + 1.20t$

   independent variable ____________________

   dependent variable ____________________

   domain ____________________

   range ____________________

2. The volume of a sphere is $\frac{4}{3}\pi$ times the cube (raised to the third power) of the radius of the sphere. The function is represented by the equation:

   $V = \frac{4}{3}\pi r^3$

   independent variable ____________________

   dependent variable ____________________

   domain ____________________

   range ____________________

Directions: For Numbers 3 and 4, determine the domain and range of the given relation. Then, determine whether the relation is a function.

3. {(−2, 4), (−1, 1), (0, 0), (1, 1), (2, 4)}

   domain { ____________________ }

   range { ____________________ }

   Is it a function? __________

4. {(−1, 5), (9, −7), (−1, 0), (−8, −6)}

   domain { ____________________ }

   range { ____________________ }

   Is it a function? __________

Directions: For Numbers 5 and 6, write the domain and range of the relation. Then, state whether the relation is a function.

5.

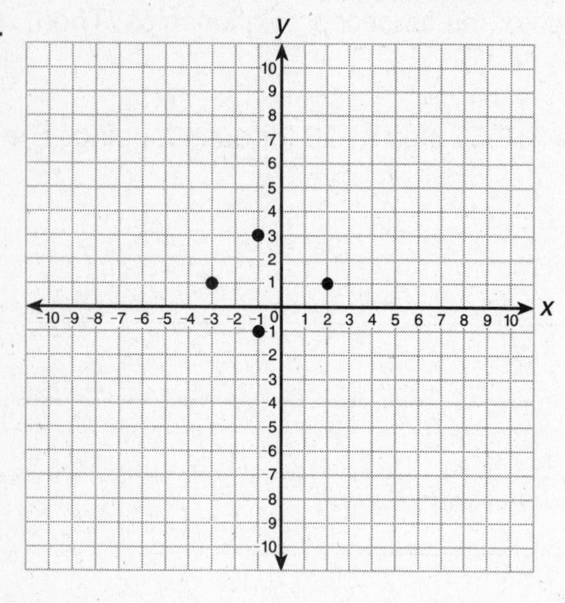

domain ____________________

range ____________________

Is it a function? __________

6.

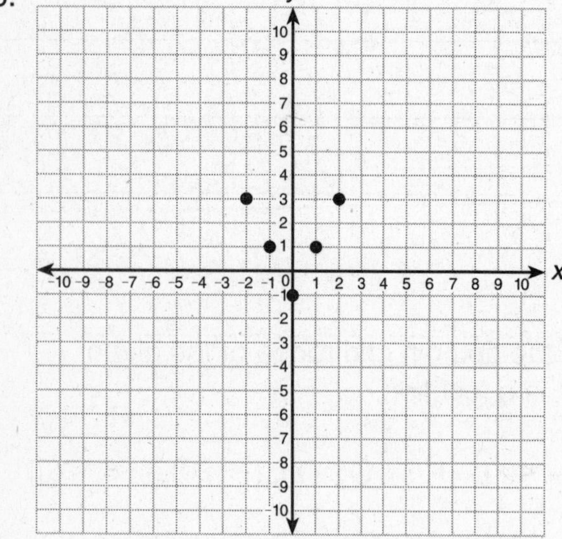

domain ____________________

range ____________________

Is it a function? __________

SATP Practice begins on the following page.

1. **What are the *domain* and *range* of the function from this table?**

x	−2	−1	0	1	2
y	11	5	3	5	11

A domain: {3, 5, 11}
range: {−2, −1, 0, 1, 2}

B domain: {−2, −1, 0}
range: {3, 5, 11}

C domain: {−2, −1, 0, 3, 5, 11}
range: {1, 2, 5, 11}

D domain: {−2, −1, 0, 1, 2}
range: {3, 5, 11}

2. **If $y = 2x - 5$ and the *domain* is {1, 2, 3, 4}, what is the *range*?**

F {2, 4, 6, 8}

G {−2, −1, 0, 1}

H {−3, −1, 1, 3}

J {−8, −6, −4, −2}

3. **Which of the following relations is a function?**

A {(3, 8), (4, 8), (5, 8)}

B {(5, 1), (5, 2), (5, 3)}

C {(8, 1), (4, 6), (4, 8)}

D {(5, 7), (5, 8), (6, 9)}

Directions: Use the following information to answer Numbers 4 through 6.

The Fishing Club is selling lures as part of a fund-raiser. For each lure that is sold, the club will earn $2. The amount that the club earns is a function of the number of lures that are sold.

4. What part of the relationship does the independent variable represent?

F The number of lures that the club has

G The amount of money the club earns

H The number of lures that are sold

J The number of members in the club

---

5. Which BEST represents the *range* of the function?

A The positive real numbers

B The positive multiples of 2

C The whole numbers

D The integers

---

6. If the club earned a total of $352, how many lures did the club sell?

F 174

G 176

H 178

J 180

Objectives: 2e

Lesson 4: Linear Equations and Inequalities in Two Variables

In this lesson, you will graph linear equations and inequalities in two variables. You will also review the properties of linear equations and use them to solve application problems.

Graphing Linear Equations

A linear equation in two variables has an infinite number of solutions. Each solution is an ordered pair with coordinates that can be substituted for the variables in the equation to make it true. If you were to plot all the solutions on a coordinate plane, they would be all the points of a straight line. So, when you graph a linear equation, you draw the line that passes through all the points with ordered pairs that are solutions to the linear equation. There are a couple of ways to graph a linear equation.

Finding Ordered Pairs

The first way to graph a linear equation is to find at least three solutions to the equation, plot the points associated with the solutions, and draw the line that passes through them. You should find at least three solutions to make sure they are **collinear** (all lie on the same line). If the solutions aren't collinear, then at least one of them is incorrect. To find solutions, pick any arbitrary value for x or y, substitute it for the variable in the equation, and solve for the remaining variable. The easiest values to pick are usually $x = 0$, $y = 0$, and then some third value for either x or y.

Example

Graph the linear equation $-x + 4y = 8$.

Pick at least three arbitrary values for x or y and solve for the remaining variable to find at least three solutions.

Let $x = 0$	Let $y = 0$	Let $x = 4$
$-x + 4y = 8$	$-x + 4y = 8$	$-x + 4y = 8$
$\mathbf{0} + 4y = 8$	$-x + 4(\mathbf{0}) = 8$	$-(\mathbf{4}) + 4y = 8$
$4y = 8$	$-x = 8$	$4y = 12$
$y = 2$	$x = -8$	$y = 3$

The following table of values shows the ordered pairs of the solutions.

x	y	Ordered Pair
0	2	(0, 2)
−8	0	(−8, 0)
4	3	(4, 3)

Plot the points from the table of values on a coordinate plane and use a straightedge to draw the line that passes through them.

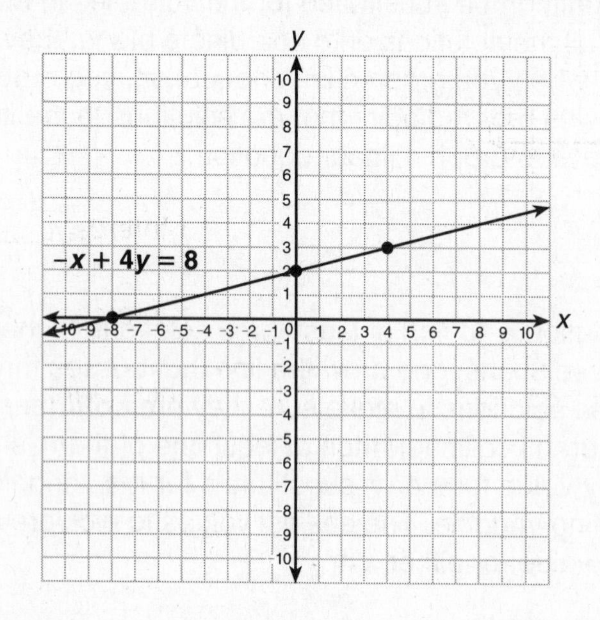

The ordered pair of any point on the line is a solution to the equation.

The intercepts of a line are the points where the line intercepts (crosses) an axis. The ***x*-intercept** is the point with the ordered pair **(*x*, 0)** where a line intercepts the *x*-axis. Similarly, the ***y*-intercept** is the point with the ordered pair **(0, *y*)** where a line intercepts the *y*-axis. In this example, the *x*-intercept is −8 and the *y*-intercept is 2.

Notice that both axes are labeled and scaled. In this case, it was not difficult to keep the scale the same on both axes. Occasionally, you will need to use different scales if the coordinates for one of the variables are much larger than the coordinates of the other variable.

It is a good idea to write the linear equation near its graph. (The equation is like a title for the graph.)

Practice

Directions: For Numbers 1 through 3, find the ordered pairs of the *x*-intercept, the *y*-intercept, and a third point of the graph of the given linear equation. Then, graph the equation.

1. $3x - 6y = -3$

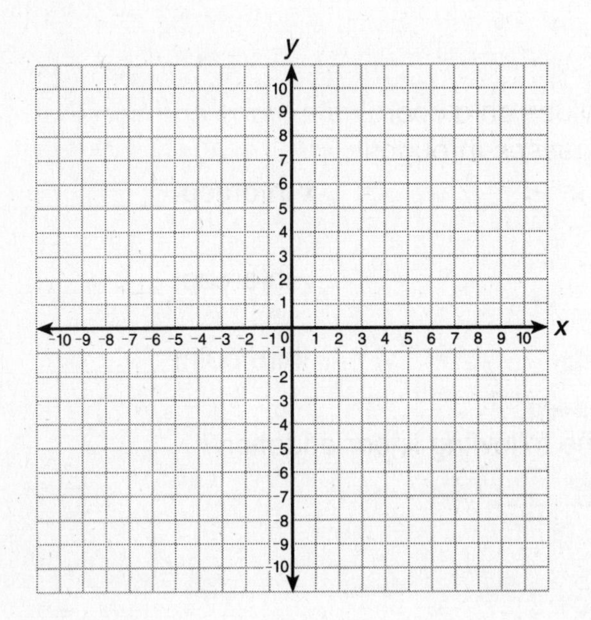

x-intercept ___________

y-intercept ___________

third point ___________

2. $4x + 2y = 12$

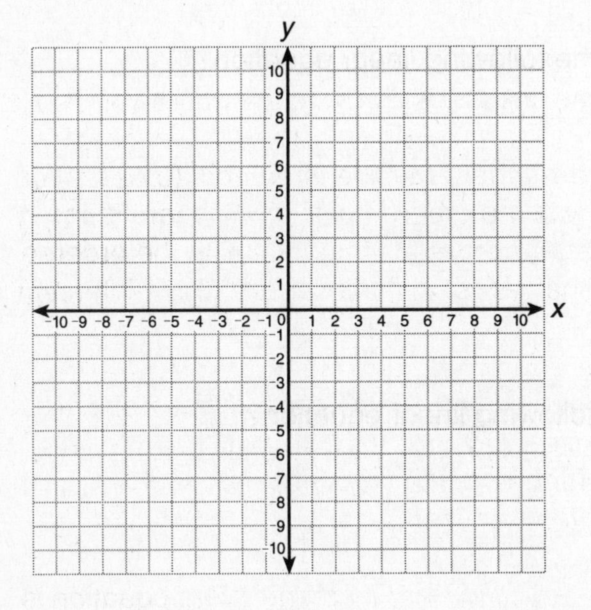

x-intercept ___________

y-intercept ___________

third point ___________

3. $-5x + 5y = -25$

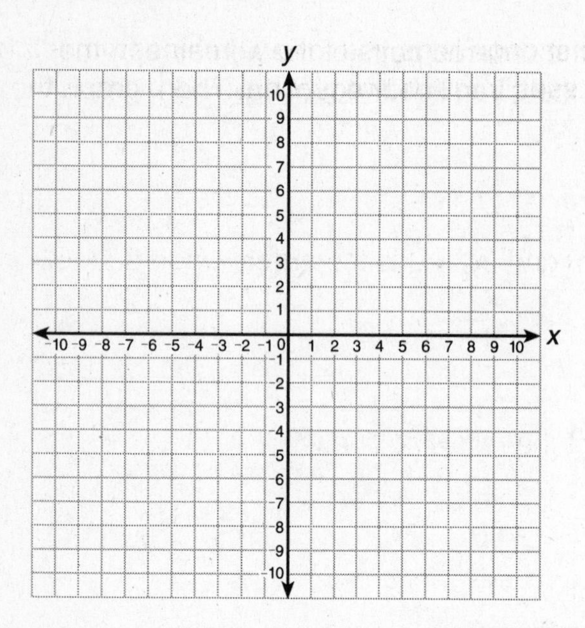

x-intercept ___________

y-intercept ___________

third point ___________

4. What is the *y*-intercept of the graph of the following linear equation?

$-2x + 5y = -10$

A. -5
B. -2
C. 2
D. 5

5. What is the *x*-intercept of the graph of the following linear equation?

$4x + 6y = 36$

A. -9
B. -8
C. 8
D. 9

6. Which ordered pair is a solution to the following linear equation?

$7x - 5y = 6$

A. (8, 10)
B. (−2, 4)
C. (3, −3)
D. (−7, 11)

Objectives: 2d, 2e, 3b, 4b

Slope

The **slope** of a line describes how steep the change is as you follow the line from left to right. You can find the slope of a line that passes through two given points using the following formula:

$$\textbf{slope} = \frac{y_2 - y_1}{x_2 - x_1} = \frac{\text{vertical change}}{\text{horizontal change}} \text{ or } \frac{\text{rise}}{\text{run}}$$

where (x_1, y_1) is the ordered pair of one point and (x_2, y_2) is the ordered pair of another point. Write the fraction in simplest form.

Example

Use the formula to find the slope of the following line.

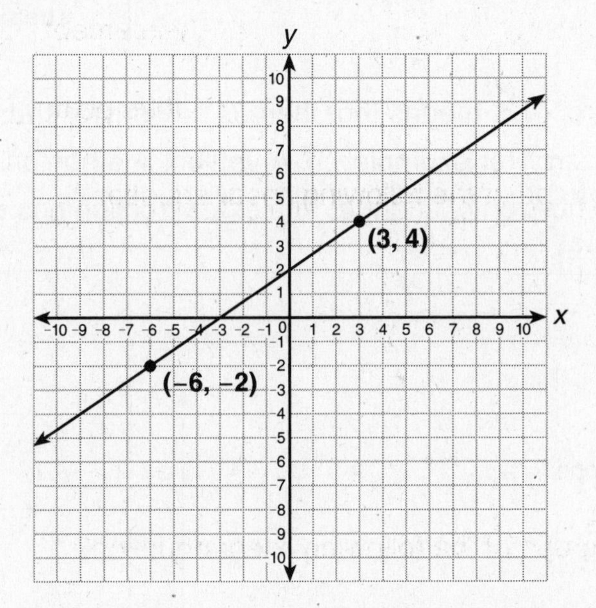

(3, 4) and (−6, −2) are the ordered pairs of two points on the line

x_1 y_1 (for 3, 4) and x_2 y_2 (for −6, −2)

$$\text{slope} = \frac{y_2 - y_1}{x_2 - x_1} = \frac{-2 - 4}{-6 - 3} = \frac{-6}{-9} = \frac{2}{3}$$

The slope of the line is $\frac{2}{3}$. The line rises as you follow it from left to right.

Knowing Slope When You See It

When you look at the graph of a line, you can tell if the line has a positive or negative slope. A line has a positive slope when it rises from left to right and a negative slope when it falls from left to right.

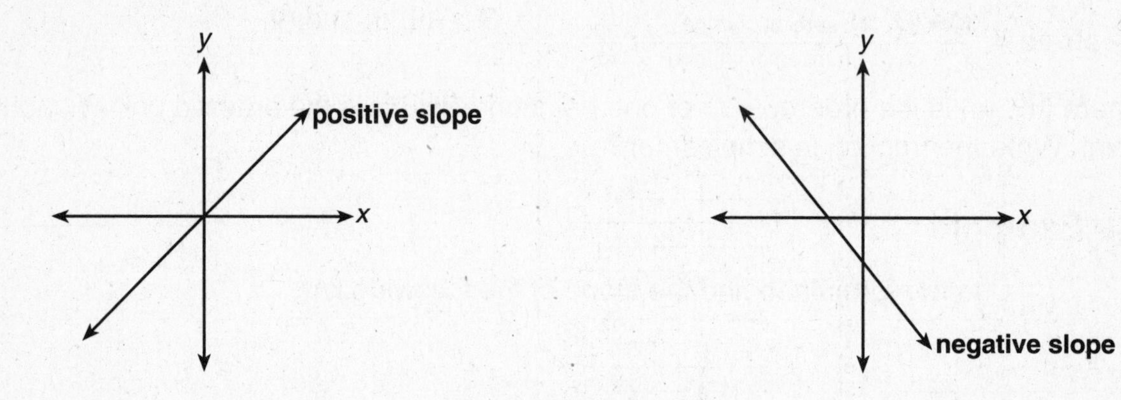

A horizontal line has a slope of zero. This means that there is no vertical change. The slope fraction has a numerator of zero $\left(\text{for example, } \frac{0}{5}\right)$. A vertical line has an undefined slope. This means that there is no horizontal change. The slope fraction has a denominator of zero $\left(\text{for example, } \frac{5}{0}\right)$.

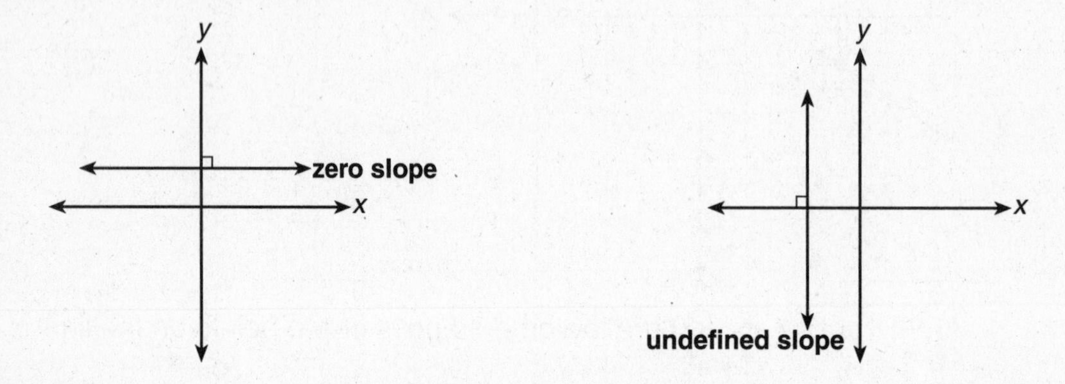

The slope also tells how steep the line is. The larger the absolute value of the slope, the steeper the line. The smaller the absolute value of the slope, the flatter the line.

Practice

Directions: For Numbers 1 through 4, find the slope of the line that passes through the given points. Then, graph the line and verify that your slope is correct.

1. $(-4, 6)$ and $(3, 4)$

slope __________

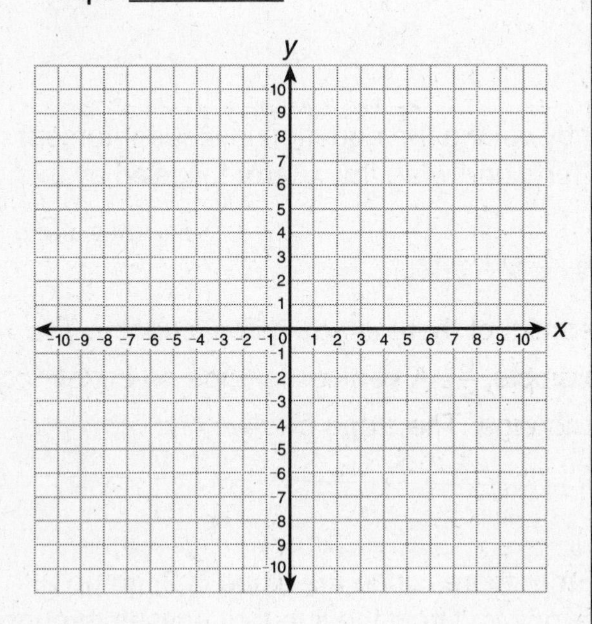

2. $(-4, 6)$ and $(-6, -2)$

slope __________

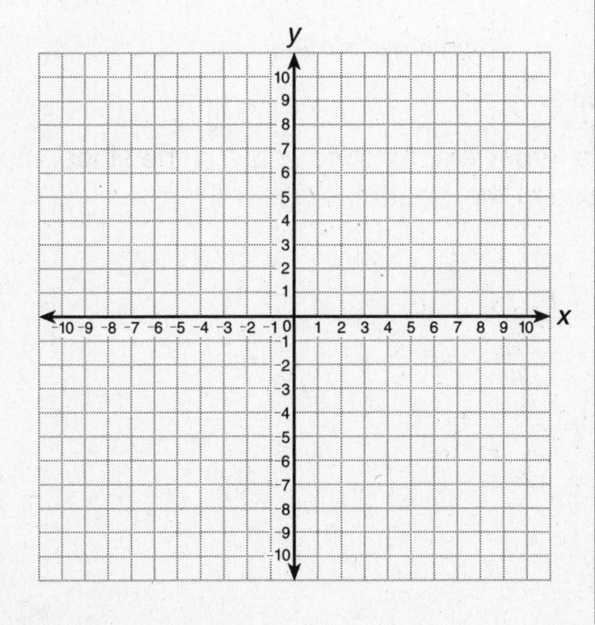

3. $(-4, 6)$ and $(4, -3)$

slope __________

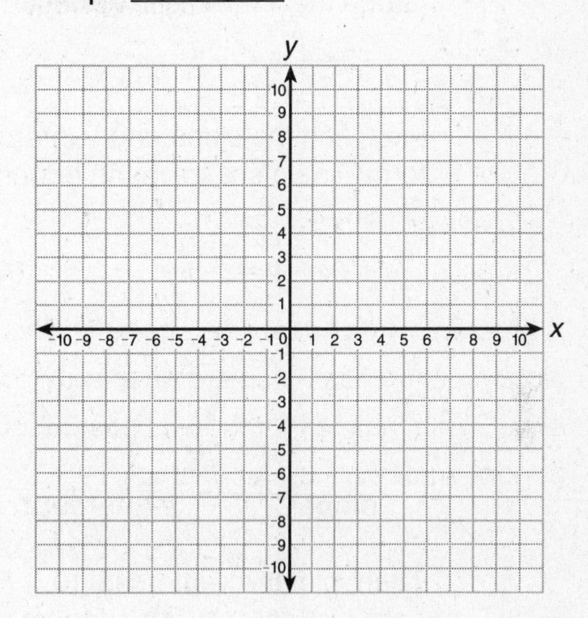

4. $(3, 4)$ and $(4, -3)$

slope __________

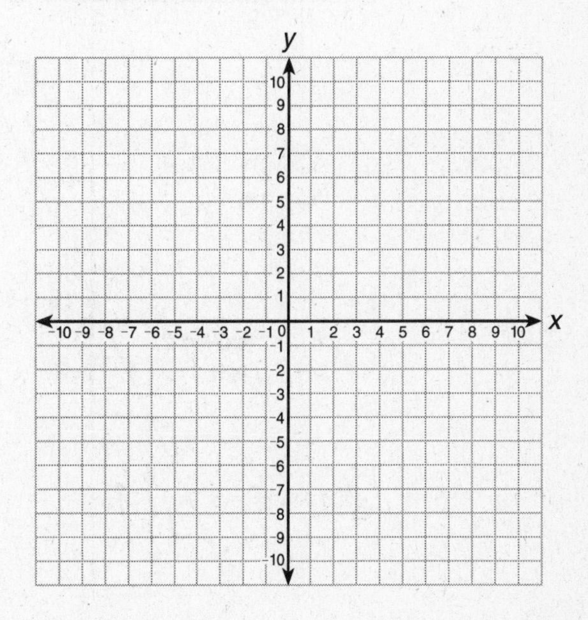

Using Slope-Intercept Form to Graph a Linear Equation

The **slope-intercept form** of a linear equation is $y = mx + b$, where m is the **slope** and b is the **y-intercept**. You can use this form to plot at least three points that are solutions to the equation, then connect them with a line to graph the equation.

Example

Graph the following linear equation.

$-2x + y = -5$

First, find the slope and y-intercept by writing the equation in slope-intercept form. To do so, solve the equation for y and write the x-term followed by the constant.

$-2x + y = -5$ (Add $2x$ to both sides.)

$y = \textcircled{2}x \textcircled{-5}$

$\downarrow \quad \downarrow$

$y = mx + b$

slope: 2 ***y*-intercept:** -5

Then, plot the y-intercept $(0, -5)$. From there, since the slope is 2, go up 2, right 1 or down 2, left 1 to plot more points. Draw the line that passes through the points you plotted.

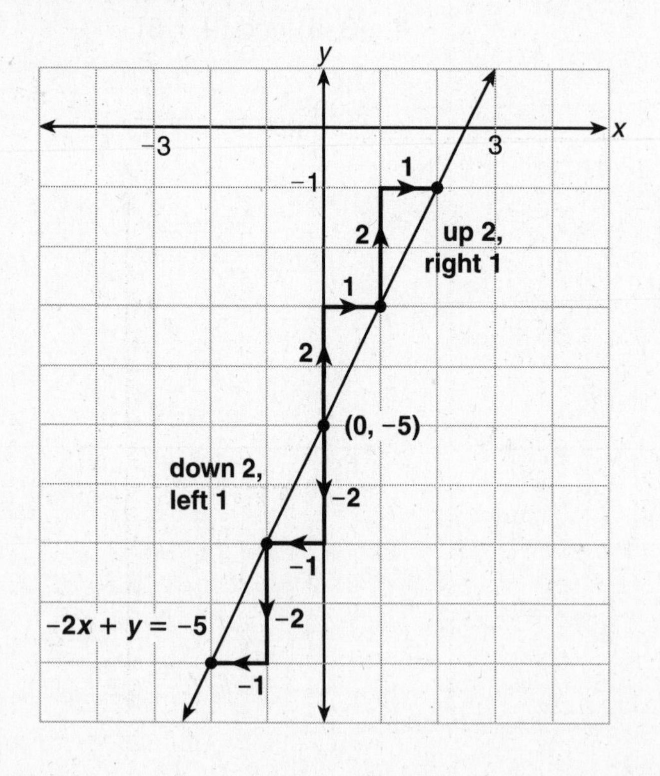

Practice

Directions: For Numbers 1 through 4, write the linear equation in slope-intercept form. Then, find the slope (*m*) and *y*-intercept (*b*), and use them to graph the given linear equation.

1. $\frac{2}{3}x + y = 8$

slope-intercept form ____________________

m __________

b __________

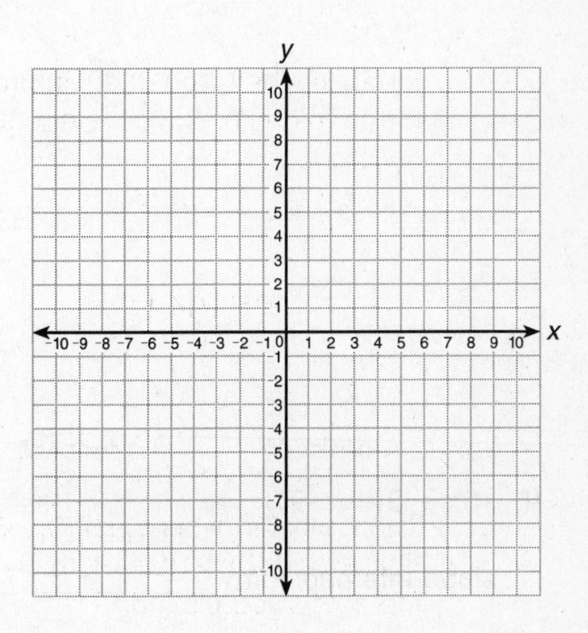

2. $-5x + y = 1$

slope-intercept form ____________________

m __________

b __________

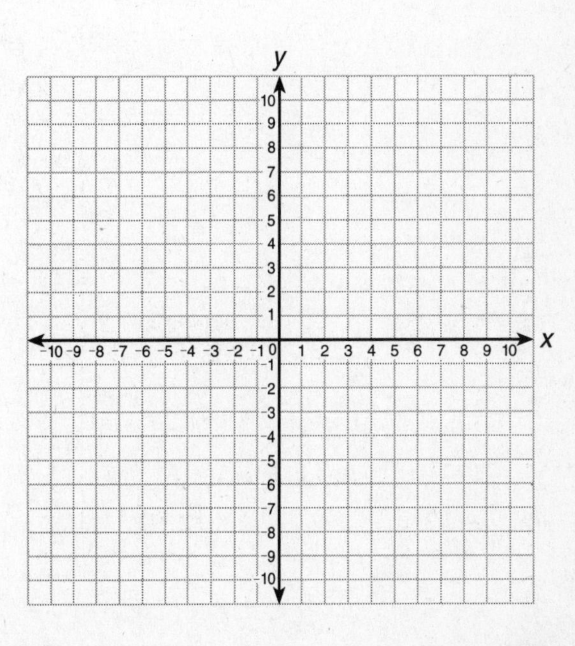

3. $x - 4y = -12$

slope-intercept form ____________________

m __________

b __________

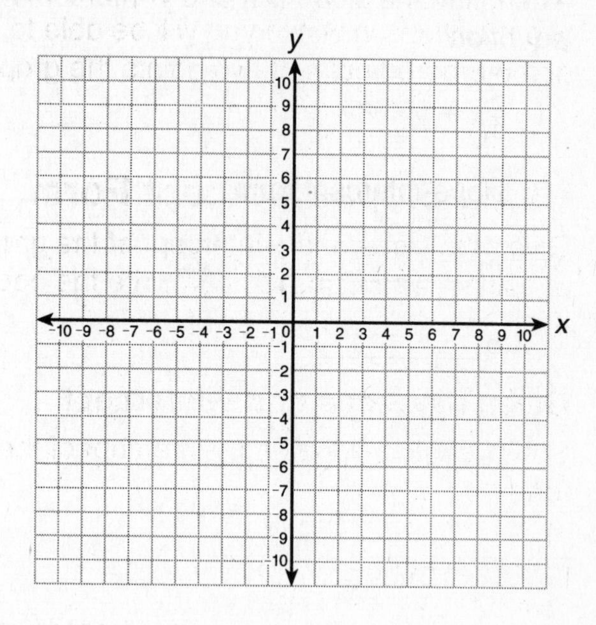

4. $15x + 3y = -9$

slope-intercept form ____________________

m __________

b __________

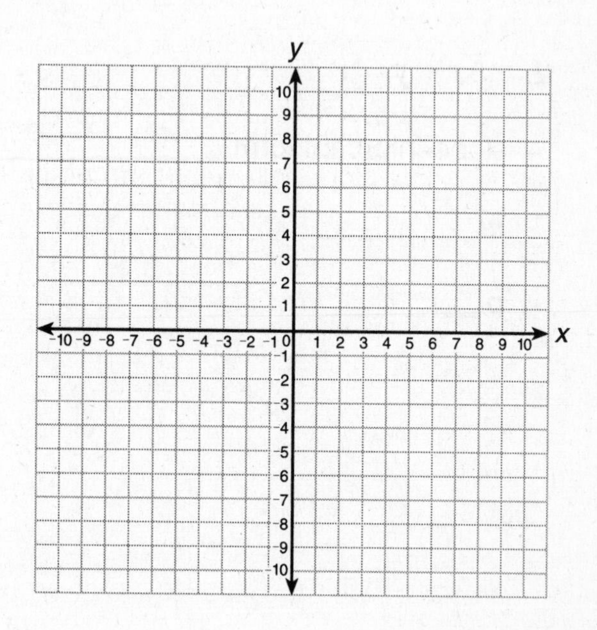

Writing Linear Equations

Depending on what information you are given about the graph of a linear equation, you can use slope-intercept form or point-slope form to write the equation. There are also two situations in which you will be able to write the linear equation by taking a close look at the ordered pairs of two points the graph passes through.

Using Slope-Intercept Form

Given the slope and *y*-intercept of the graph of a linear equation, or given just the graph of a linear equation, you can write the equation using the slope-intercept form.

Given the Slope and *y*-Intercept

Substitute the slope and *y*-intercept of the graph for the variables in the slope-intercept form.

What is the slope-intercept form of the linear equation whose graph has a slope of 3 and a *y*-intercept of -4?

Substitute the values into the slope-intercept form.

$$y = mx + b$$

$$y = \mathbf{3}x + (\mathbf{-4})$$

$$y = 3x - 4$$

The slope-intercept form of the linear equation is $y = 3x - 4$.

Given the Graph

From the graph of a linear equation, find the slope and *y*-intercept. Then, substitute them for the variables in the slope-intercept form.

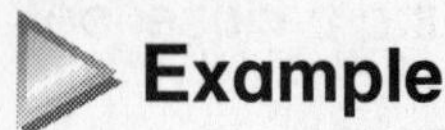

Example

What is the slope-intercept form of the linear equation whose graph is shown on the coordinate plane?

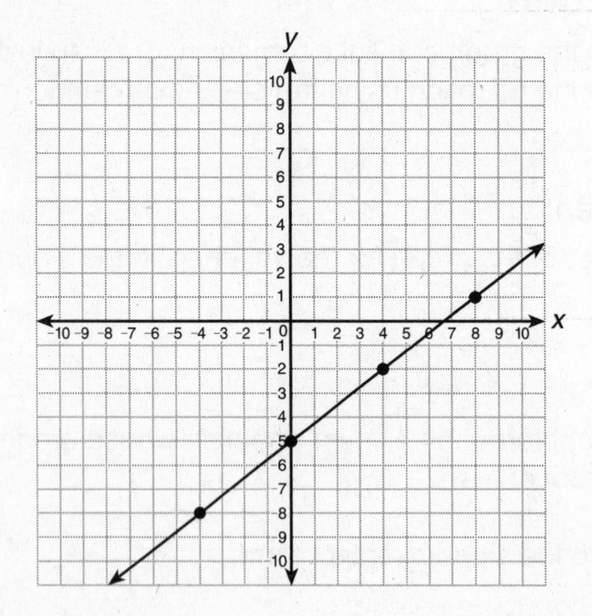

Find the slope of the line. The points with ordered pairs (0, −5) and (4, −2) are on the line.

$$m = \frac{y_2 - y_1}{x_2 - x_1} = \frac{-2 - (-5)}{4 - 0} = \frac{3}{4}$$

The slope is $\frac{3}{4}$.

Next, find the *y*-intercept. The line intercepts the *y*-axis at (0, −5).

$$b = -5$$

The *y*-intercept is −5.

Substitute the values of the slope and *y*-intercept into the slope-intercept form.

$$y = \frac{3}{4}x - 5$$

The slope-intercept form of the linear equation is $y = \frac{3}{4}x - 5$.

Practice

Directions: For Numbers 1 through 5, write the slope-intercept form of the linear equation whose graph has the given slope and *y*-intercept.

1. slope: $-\frac{1}{3}$

   y-intercept: $\frac{3}{5}$

   slope-intercept form ____________________

2. slope: 3

   y-intercept: -4.25

   slope-intercept form ____________________

3. slope: -1.75

   y-intercept: 3.1

   slope-intercept form ____________________

4. slope: -1

   y-intercept: 1

   slope-intercept form ____________________

5. slope: $\frac{2}{3}$

   y-intercept: $-\frac{5}{6}$

   slope-intercept form ____________________

Directions: For Numbers 6 through 9, write the slope-intercept form of the linear equation whose graph is given.

6.

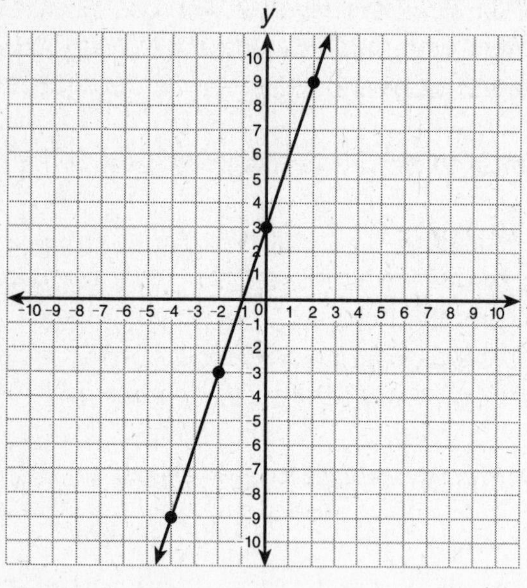

slope-intercept form ______________

7.

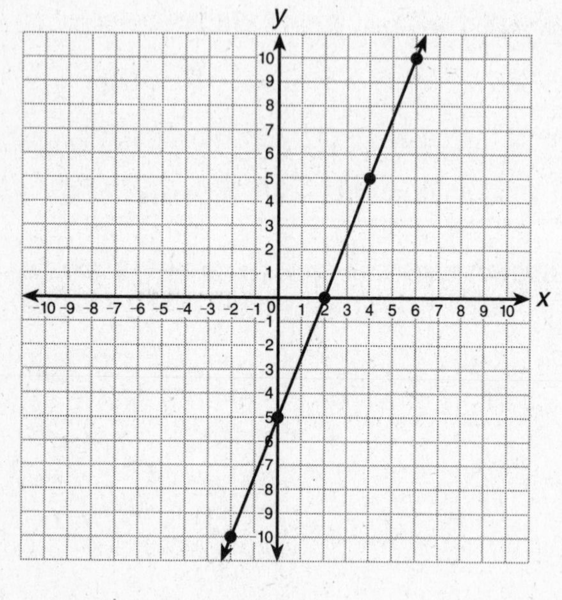

slope-intercept form ______________

8.

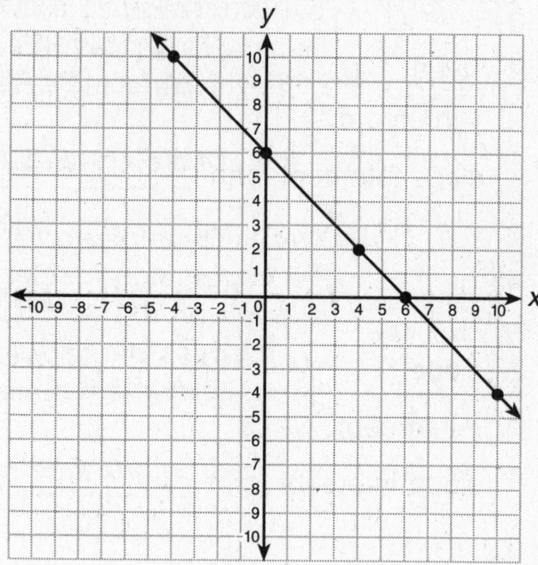

slope-intercept form ______________

9.

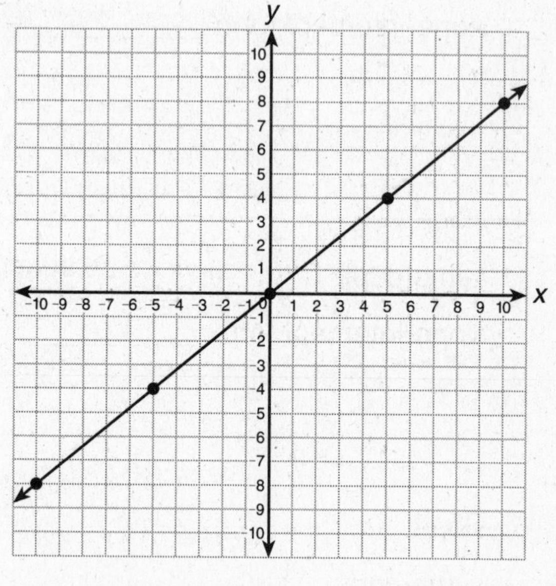

slope-intercept form ______________

Objectives: 2e

Using Point-Slope Form

Given the ordered pair of a point on the graph and the slope of the graph of a linear equation, or given the ordered pairs of two points on the graph of a linear equation, you can write the equation in **point-slope form**. Here is point-slope form:

$\mathbf{y - y_1 = m(x - x_1)}$ where (x_1, y_1) is the ordered pair of a point and m is the slope.

Given the Ordered Pair of a Point and the Slope

Substitute the coordinates of the point and the slope for the variables in point-slope form and solve for y. This will give the linear equation in slope-intercept form.

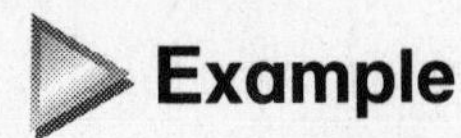

Example

What is the slope-intercept form of the linear equation whose graph passes through $(-1, 3)$ with a slope of -4?

Substitute into point-slope form and solve for y.

$$y - y_1 = m(x - x_1)$$
$$y - 3 = -4[x - (-1)]$$
$$y - 3 = -4x - 4$$
$$y = -4x - 1$$

(This is slope-intercept form.)

Graph the linear equation to verify that your equation is correct.

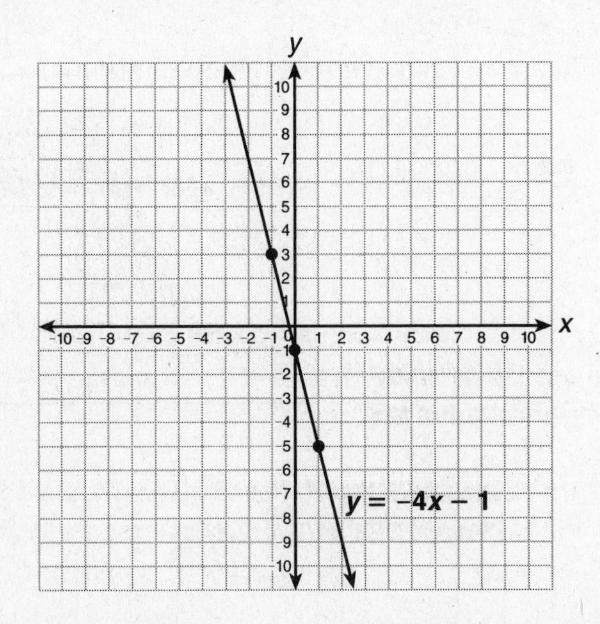

The slope-intercept form of the linear equation is $y = -4x - 1$.

Practice

Directions: For Numbers 1 through 4, use point-slope form to write the slope-intercept form of the linear equation whose graph passes through the point with the given ordered pair and has the given slope. Then, graph the line to verify that your equation is correct.

1. $(3, -1)$; $m = -\frac{1}{3}$

slope-intercept form ______________

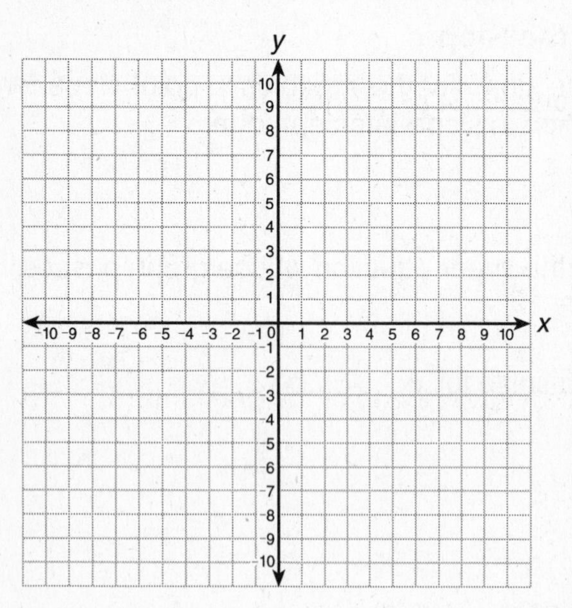

3. $(-8, 5)$; $m = 0$

slope-intercept form ______________

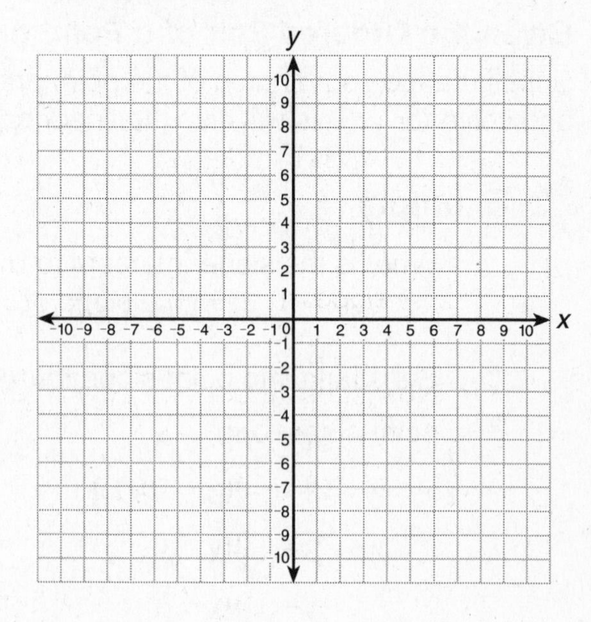

2. $(4, 6)$; $m = 3$

slope-intercept form ______________

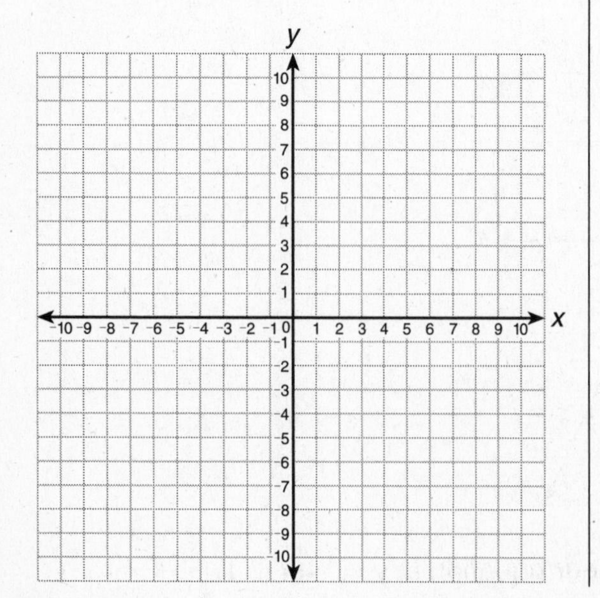

4. $(-1, 3)$; $m = -4$

slope-intercept form ______________

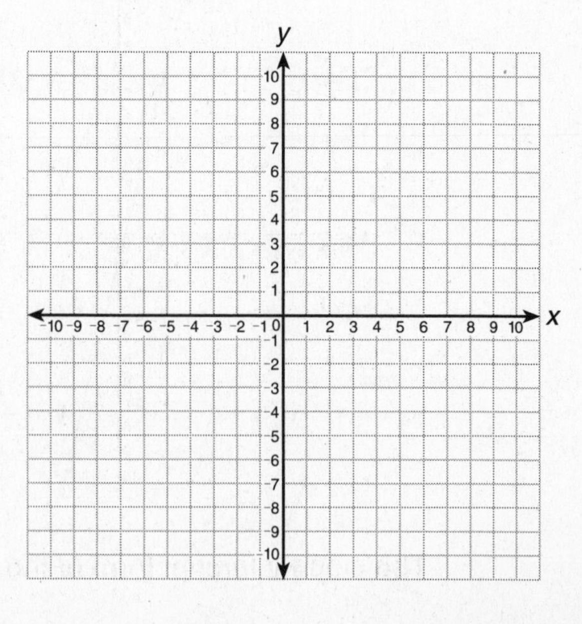

Objectives: 2e

Given the Ordered Pairs of Two Points

First, you need to find the slope of the line that passes through the two points. Use the slope formula from page 51. After you find the slope, substitute the coordinates of either point and the slope for the variables in point-slope form and solve for *y*. This will give the linear equation in slope-intercept form.

Example

What is the slope-intercept form of the linear equation whose graph passes through (0, 7) and (2, 3)?

To find slope, use (0, 7) as (x_1, y_1) and (2, 3) as (x_2, y_2).

$$\begin{array}{cc} (x_1, y_1) & (x_2, y_2) \\ \downarrow\ \ \downarrow & \downarrow\ \ \downarrow \\ (0,\ 7) & (2,\ 3) \end{array}$$

slope: $m = \frac{y_2 - y_1}{x_2 - x_1} = \frac{3 - 7}{2 - 0} = \frac{-4}{2} = -2$

Now substitute $m = -2$ and the coordinates of one of the points, (0, 7), into point-slope form.

$y - 7 = -2(x - 0)$

$y - 7 = -2x$

$y = -2x + 7$ (This is slope-intercept form.)

Graph the linear equation to verify that your equation is correct.

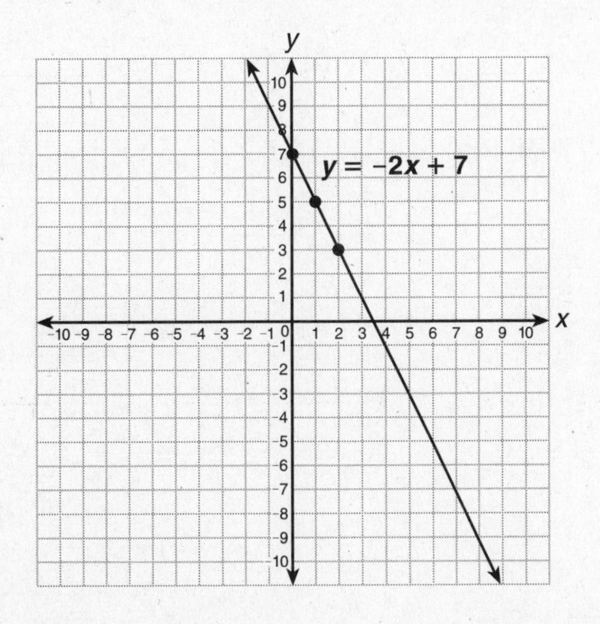

The slope-intercept form of the linear equation is $y = -2x + 7$.

Same *x*-Coordinate, Different *y*-Coordinates
The difference of the *x*-coordinates is zero, so the denominator of the slope fraction is zero (the numerator is some constant not equal to zero). In this situation, the slope is undefined, and the graph is a vertical line. The linear equation will have the form $x = a$, where a is the *x*-coordinate of the points.

Example

What is the linear equation whose graph passes through (**5**, 2) and (**5**, −5)?

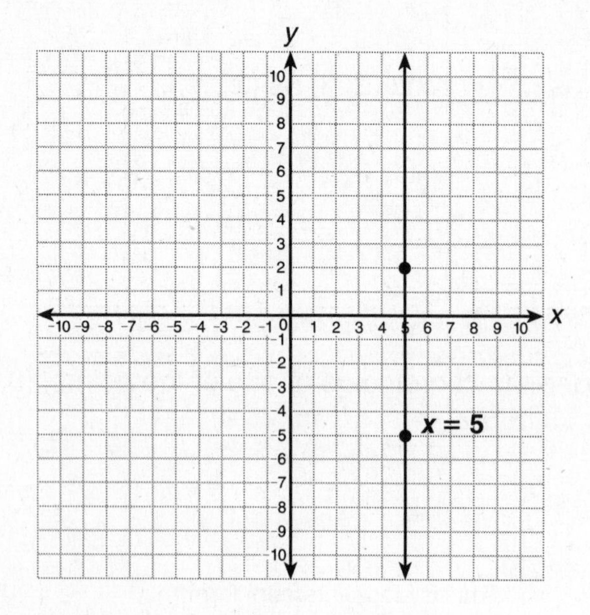

The linear equation is $x = 5$.

Practice

Directions: For Numbers 1 through 4, write the slope-intercept form of the linear equation whose graph passes through the points with the given ordered pairs. Then, graph the line to verify that your equation is correct.

1. (8, 9) and (8, 6)

slope-intercept form ______________

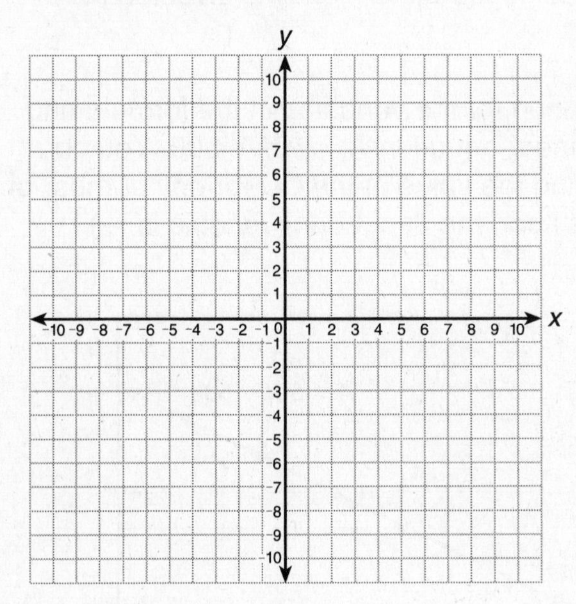

2. (6, 3) and (5, 2)

slope-intercept form ______________

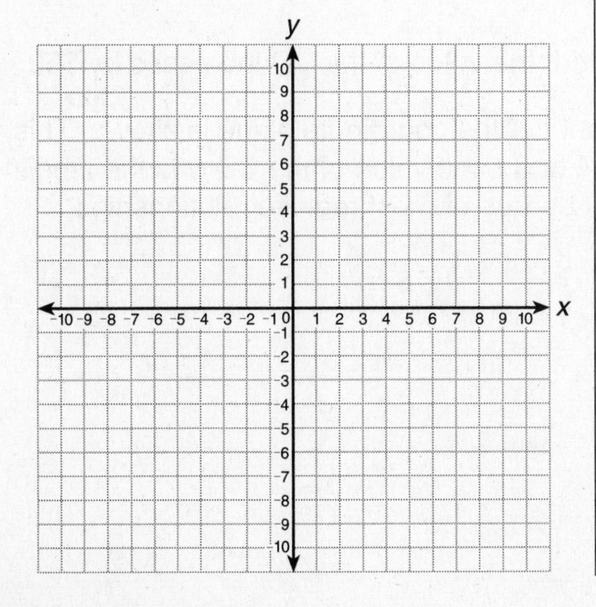

3. (10, 3) and (0, −2)

slope-intercept form ______________

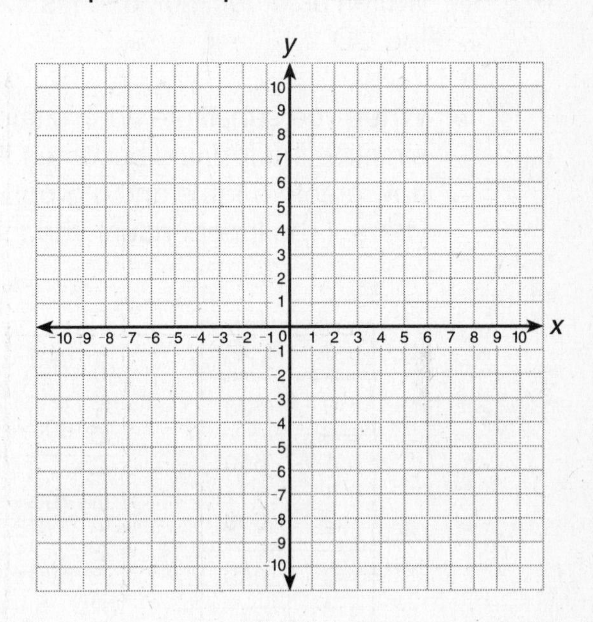

4. (1, 4) and (3, −4)

slope-intercept form ______________

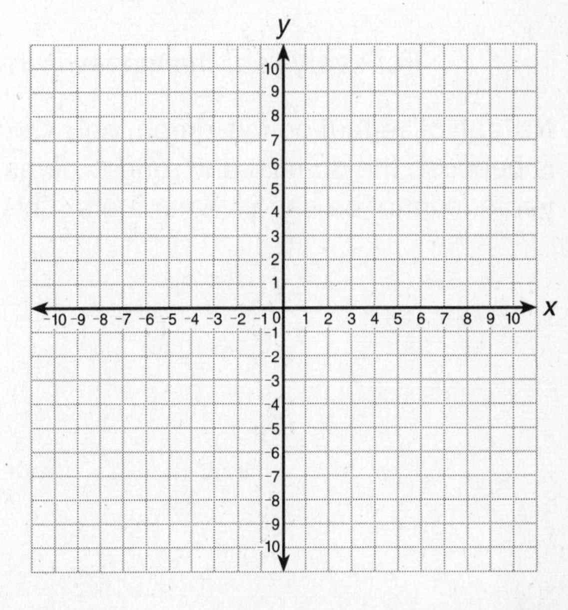

Applications of Linear Equations

There are many real-life applications of linear equations.

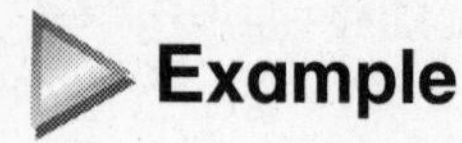

Example

John is investing \$500 into a certificate of deposit (CD) that earns 10% simple interest per year. The formula for finding the value of the CD is $A = Prt + P$, where A is the value of the CD, P is the amount invested, r is the interest rate written as a decimal, and t is the time in years the money is invested in the CD.

When you substitute John's information for the variables in the formula and simplify, the formula becomes the linear equation $A = 50t + 500$. You can now create a table and a graph to find the value of the CD for any number of years. (The independent variable is t and the dependent variable is A.)

t	A
0	500
1	550
2	600
3	650
4	700
5	750
6	800

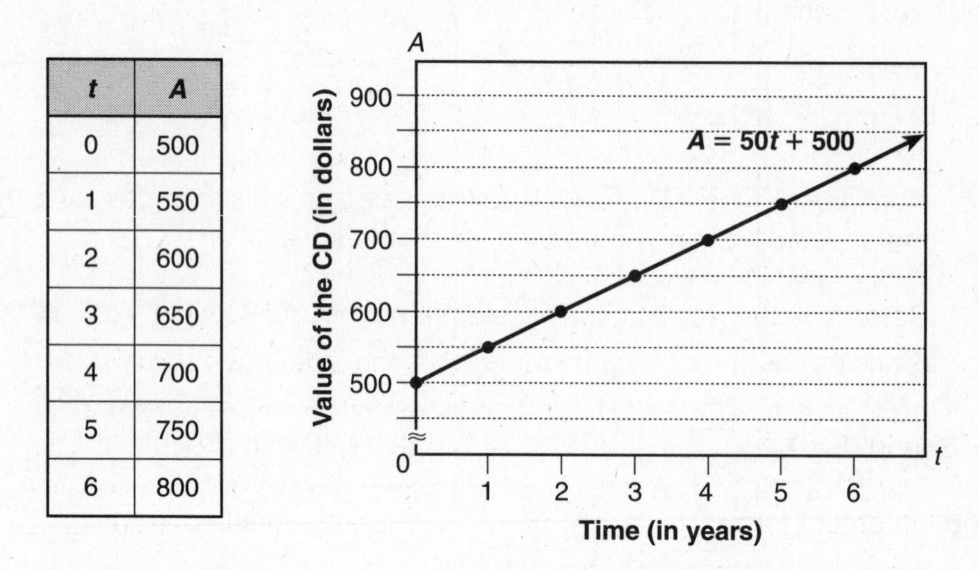

For every year the money is invested, the value of the CD increases by \$50.

Note: Notice that on this graph, only Quadrant I of the coordinate plane is shown. This is because the domain and range values of A and t, the value of the CD and the time in years, cannot be negative numbers. This will be true of most real-life relationships.

Objectives: 2d, 2e, 3b

There are times when you might be given a table that shows a relationship between two quantities and have to determine whether the relationship represents a linear equation. The relationship represents a linear equation if there is a constant rate of change in the table. If the relationship is linear, you can write the equation that represents the relationship to help answer questions.

Example

During a carnival, each person can play games to earn points which can be traded for prize tickets. Even if a person doesn't play any games, he or she gets a certain number of tickets. The following table shows the number of tickets a person gets for earning certain numbers of points.

Points	Tickets
50	125
100	150
200	200
500	350

Does the number of prize tickets that a person gets and the number of points that a person earns represent a linear relationship?

Determine the rate of change (slope) that occurs between rows of the table. Since the number of points represents the independent variable and the number of tickets represents the dependent variable, write the rates as $\frac{\text{change in tickets}}{\text{change in points}}$.

	Points	Tickets	
	50	125	
50			25
	100	150	
100			50
	200	200	
300			150
	500	350	

$$\frac{25}{50} = \frac{50}{100} = \frac{150}{300} = \frac{1}{2}$$

Since there is a constant rate of change, $\frac{1}{2}$, the number of prize tickets that a person gets and the number of points that a person earns represents a linear relationship.

What is the linear equation that represents the relationship?

Start with the slope-intercept form of a general linear equation, where t is the number of tickets that a person gets, p is the number of points that a person earns, m is the slope (rate of change), and b is the y-intercept.

$$t = mp + b$$

Substitute any of the ordered pairs from the table for t and p and substitute $\frac{1}{2}$ for m in the formula above. Then, solve for b.

$$\mathbf{125} = \left(\tfrac{1}{2}\right)(\mathbf{50}) + b$$

$$125 = 25 + b$$

$$100 = b$$

The linear equation that represents the relationship is $t = \frac{1}{2}p + 100$.

How many tickets does each person get even if he or she doesn't play any games?

If a person doesn't play any games, then he or she can't earn any points. Therefore, find the value of t when $p = 0$.

$$t = \tfrac{1}{2}p + 100$$

$$= \tfrac{1}{2}(\mathbf{0}) + 100$$

$$= 100$$

Each person gets 100 tickets.

What does the rate of change of $\frac{1}{2}$ represent in this situation?

It means for every 2 points that a person earns, he or she gets 1 additional prize ticket.

Practice

1. A plumber charges $15 per hour, *h*, plus a $25 service fee for house calls. Write a linear equation to show how to find the total cost, *c*, of the plumber's services for house calls.

   ____

   Fill in the table and graph the line that represents the total cost.

h	*c*
1	
3	
5	
7	

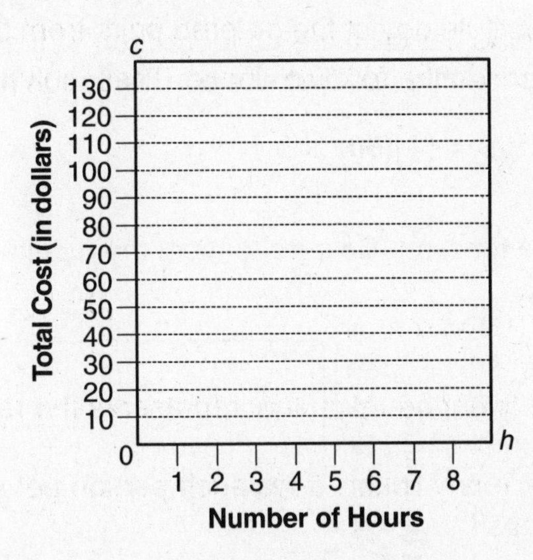

Directions: Use the following information to answer Numbers 2 through 10.

The following table shows Julie's long-distance bill for the past five months. The bill includes a monthly charge plus the charge per minute for long-distance calls.

Number of Minutes	Amount of Bill (in dollars)
150	22.50
90	19.50
115	20.75
100	20.00

2. What is the rate of change? ______________________

3. What does the rate of change represent in the situation?

   ____

4. What is the monthly charge that Julie has to pay? ______________________

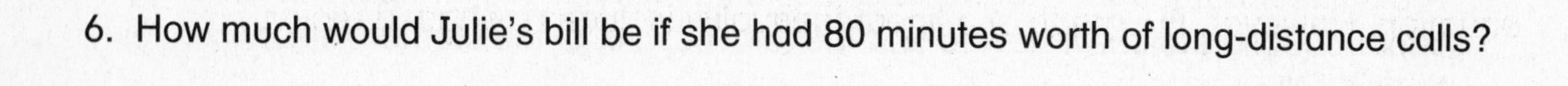

5. Write a linear function that represents the situation. ____________

6. How much would Julie's bill be if she had 80 minutes worth of long-distance calls?

____

7. If Julie wants her bill to be no more than $25, what is the maximum number of long-distance minutes that she can use each month?

____

8. Graph the function. Be sure to label the axes with the variables that you used in Number 5.

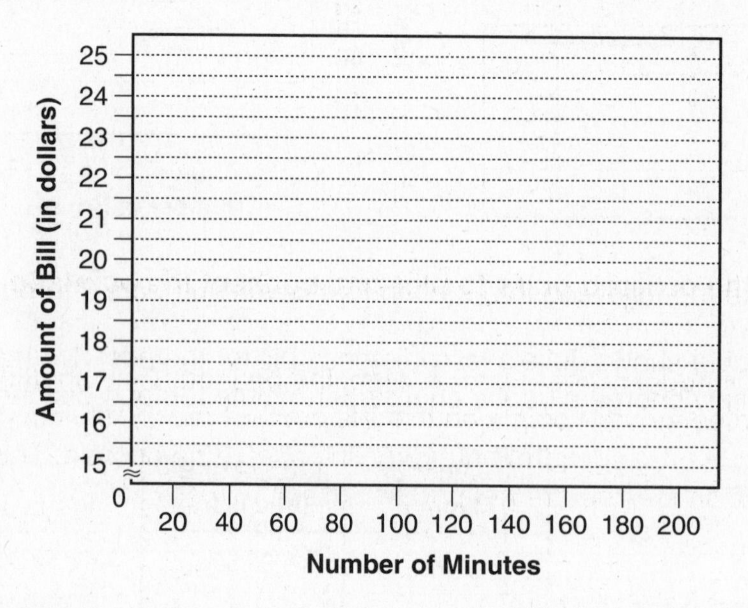

9. If the company raised Julie's charge per minute to $0.10, how would the graph in Number 8 be affected?

____

____

10. If the company raised Julie's monthly charge to $20, how would the graph in Number 8 be affected?

____

____

Objectives: 2I

Graphing Linear Inequalities

You can graph a linear inequality in much the same way that you graph a linear equation. However, the graph of a linear inequality includes a shaded region.

Example

Graph the inequality $x + 4y > 8$.

Step 1: **Replace the inequality symbol with an equal sign.** (This is the equation of the boundary line.)

$x + 4y = 8$

Step 2: **Make a table of ordered pairs that are solutions to the equation of the boundary line.**

x	*y*
0	2
4	1
8	0

Step 3: **Use the ordered pairs to plot and connect the points to form a boundary line.**

If the inequality has a $\geq$ or $\leq$ sign, the boundary line should be solid. This indicates that the points on the line are part of the solution. If the inequality has a $>$ or $<$ sign, the boundary line should be dashed. This indicates that the points on the line are not part of the solution.

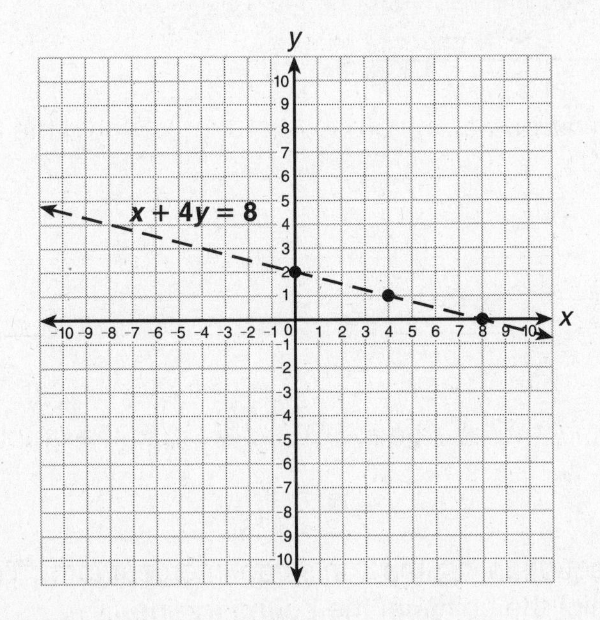

Step 4: **Select a test point not on the line.**

A test point is any ordered pair that is not on the boundary line. (0, 0) is always a good choice for a test point if it is not on the boundary line. Substitute the coordinates of the test point for *x* and *y* in the inequality.

$$x + 4y > 8$$

$$\mathbf{0} + 4(\mathbf{0}) > 8$$

$$0 + 0 > 8$$

$$0 > 8$$

Since 0 is not greater than 8, the test point (0, 0) makes the inequality false.

Step 5: **Shade the correct side of the boundary line.**

If the test point makes the inequality true, shade the side of the boundary line where the test point is located.

If the test point makes the inequality false, shade the side of the boundary line opposite the test point.

In this example, the shading is on the side of the boundary line opposite the test point. Any point in the shaded region is a solution to the inequality.

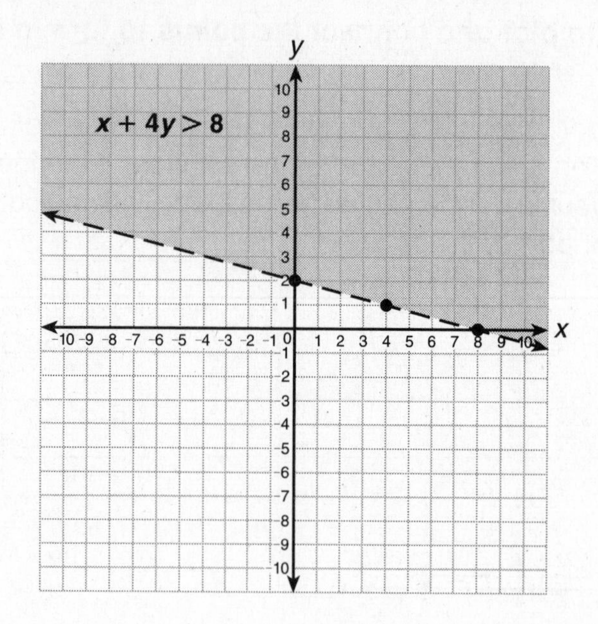

TIP: You can also write the equation in Step 1 in slope-intercept form. Then, use the slope and *y*-intercept to plot the points of the boundary line.

Practice

Directions: For Numbers 1 and 2, graph the inequality. Then, fill in the table with three ordered pairs that are solutions to the linear inequality.

1. $x - y < 2$

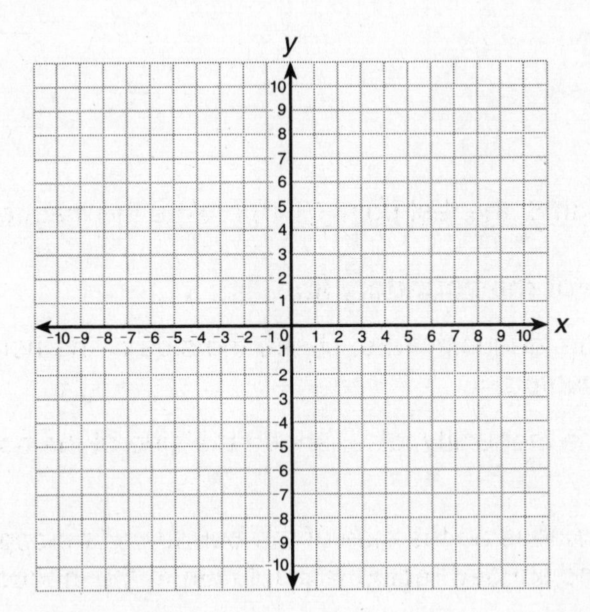

x	y

2. $\frac{1}{2}x - y \geq -1$

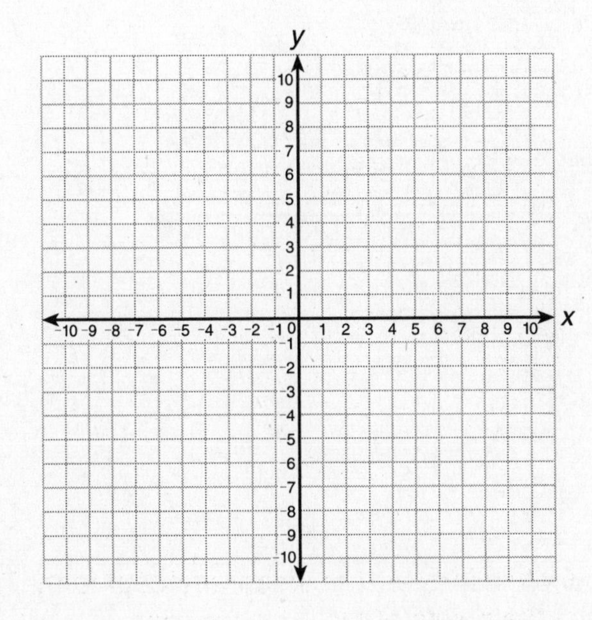

x	y

Directions: For Numbers 3 and 4, write whether or not the graph represents the given linear inequality. Then, explain why or why not on the lines below the graph.

3. $5x + 3y \leq 15$

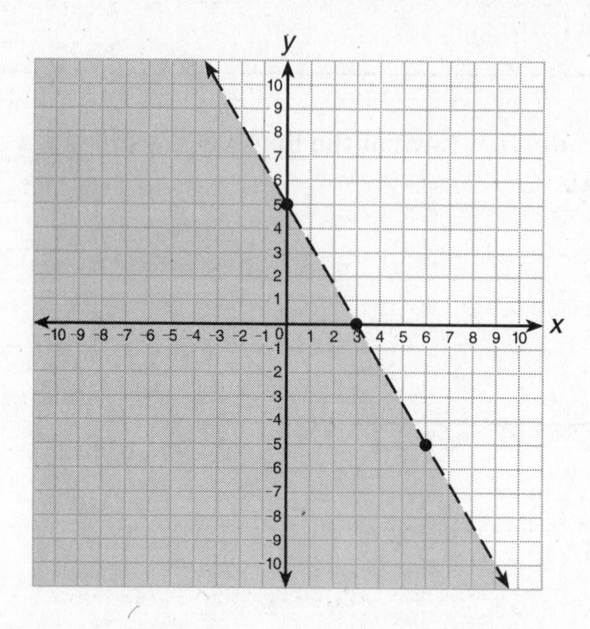

---

4. $6x - 9y > 36$

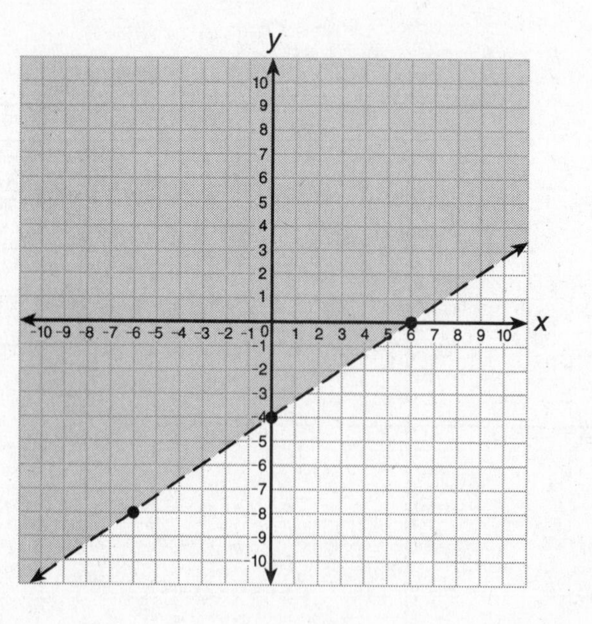

SATP Practice begins on the following page.

1. Which set of ordered pairs are solutions to the linear equation $-4x + y = 6$?

A $(-3, -22), (-1, -2), (1, 2)$

B $(-5, -34), (2, 8), (6, 32)$

C $(-1, 2), (0, -4), (1, -2)$

D $(-1, 2), (0, 6), (1, 10)$

---

2. What is the slope-intercept form of the linear equation with a graph that passes through $(-4, 7)$ and $(6, -8)$?

F $y = -\frac{3}{2}x + 1$

G $y = -2x + 4$

H $y = -\frac{1}{2}x - 5$

J $y = \frac{2}{3}x - 12$

---

3. Which linear inequality does the following graph represent?

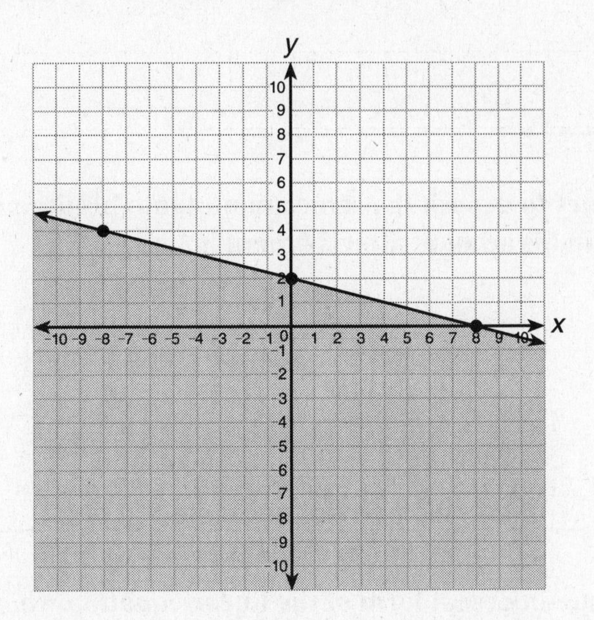

A $x + 4y < 8$

B $x + 4y > 8$

C $x + 4y \leq 8$

D $x + 4y \geq 8$

Directions: Use the following information to answer Numbers 4 and 5.

John has been depositing the same amount each month into his savings account for the last year. The following graph represents this information.

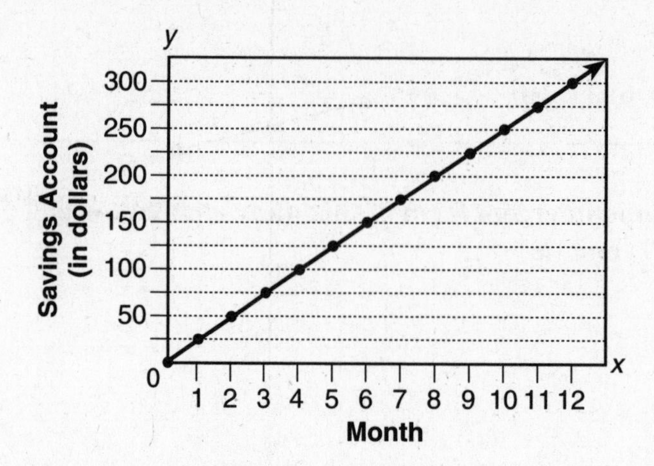

4. What amount has John been depositing into his savings account each month for the last year?

F $15

G $20

H $25

J $30

---

5. If John continues to deposit the same amount into his account each month, how much money will be in his account after 24 months?

A $600

B $540

C $480

D $420

---

6. What is the slope-intercept form of the linear equation whose graph has a slope of $\frac{3}{5}$ and a *y*-intercept of $-\frac{1}{2}$?

F $y = \frac{3}{5}x + \frac{1}{2}$

G $y = \frac{3}{5}x - \frac{1}{2}$

H $y = \frac{1}{2}x - \frac{3}{5}$

J $y = -\frac{1}{2}x + \frac{3}{5}$

---

7. What is the slope-intercept form of the linear equation shown below?

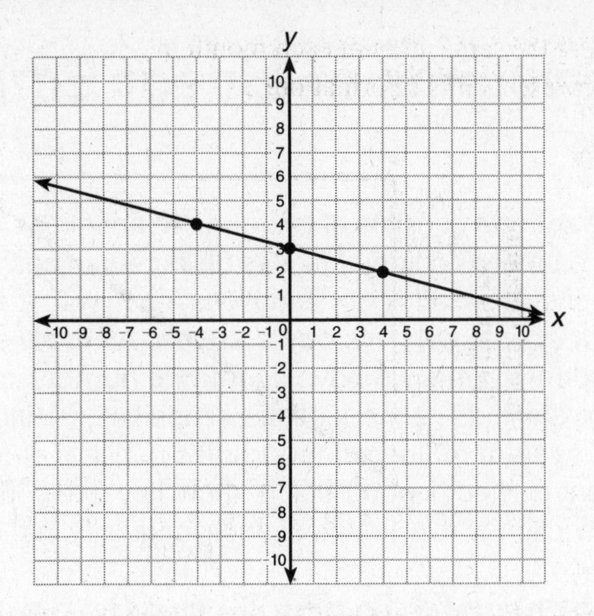

A $y = -\frac{1}{4}x - 3$

B $y = -\frac{1}{4}x + 3$

C $y = \frac{1}{4}x - 3$

D $y = \frac{1}{4}x + 3$

---

8. In the equation $y = 2(x + 12)$, how much larger is the value of y when x changes from -5 to 5?

F 20

G 32

H 44

J 56

---

9. What is the slope-intercept form of the linear equation whose graph passes through (3, −5) with a slope of $\frac{2}{3}$?

A $y = \frac{2}{3}x + 6\frac{1}{3}$

B $y = \frac{2}{3}x + 7$

C $y = \frac{2}{3}x - 6\frac{1}{3}$

D $y = \frac{2}{3}x - 7$

Lesson 5: Systems of Linear Equations and Inequalities

A **system of linear equations** consists of two or more equations. A solution to a system of linear equations is an ordered pair that makes all the equations in the system true. There are three types of systems of linear equations, each with a different number of solutions. A **consistent** system will have **one solution**. An **inconsistent** system will have **no solution**. A **dependent** system will have an **infinite number of solutions**. There are three ways to solve a system of linear equations: graphically, using substitution, or using linear combinations. A **system of linear inequalities** consists of two or more inequalities. The solution to a system of linear inequalities is shown by a region on a graph. This region will be the intersection of the graphs of each inequality in the system.

Solving Systems of Linear Equations Graphically

To solve a system of linear equations graphically, graph each equation on the same coordinate plane. The solution(s) will be the ordered pair(s) of the point(s) where all the graphs intersect. The slope and *y*-intercept of the graph of each equation will determine the type of system.

Consistent system

- exactly one solution
- different slopes

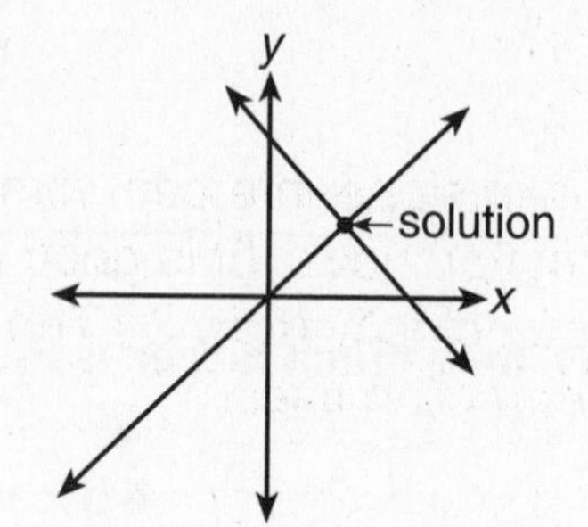

Inconsistent system

- no solution
- same slopes, different *y*-intercepts

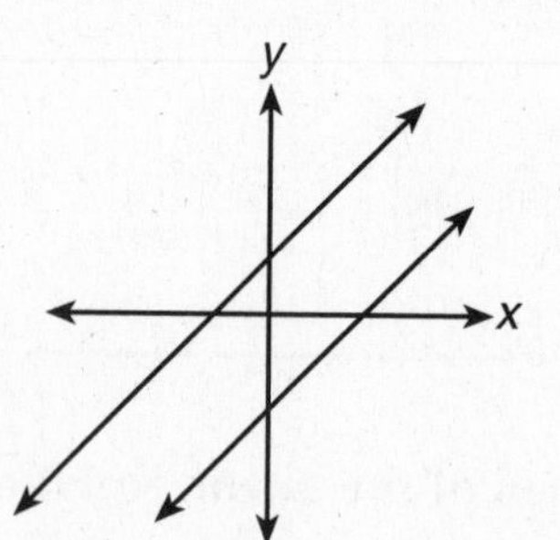

Dependent system

- infinite number of solutions
- same slopes, same *y*-intercepts

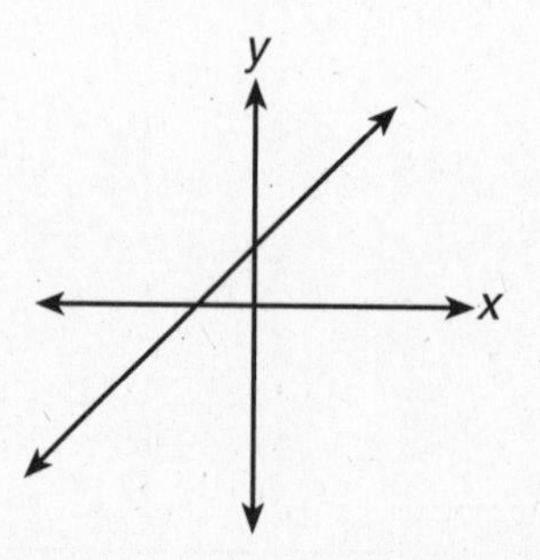

Objectives: 2f

Consistent System

A consistent system has exactly one solution. The lines intersect at one point.

Example

Solve the following system of linear equations graphically.

$2x + y = 8$
$x + 3y = 9$

Step 1: **Write each equation in slope-intercept form.**

$2x + y = 8$

$y = -2x + 8$

slope: -2

***y*-intercept:** 8

$x + 3y = 9$

$3y = -x + 9$

$y = -\frac{1}{3}x + 3$

slope: $-\frac{1}{3}$

***y*-intercept:** 3

Since each equation is in slope-intercept form, you have a better perspective on what type of system you have. (It is good to have an idea of what the graph will look like before you actually draw it.) The slopes are different, so the graph will show a pair of intersecting lines.

Step 2: **Plot each y-intercept. Then, find a few other points and draw the graph of each equation.**

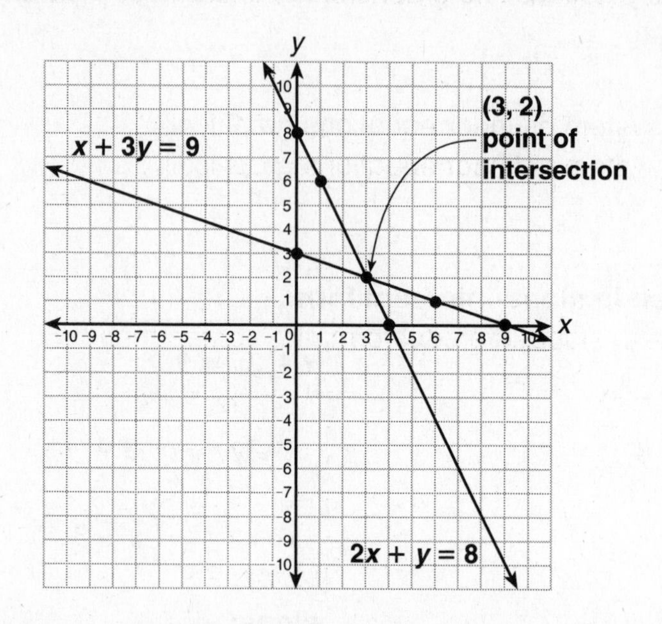

The two lines appear to intersect at (3, 2). This is a possible solution, but you need to check to see that it makes both equations true.

Step 3: **Check the point of intersection.**

Substitute the values of the ordered pair (3, 2) into both original equations to see if they make the equations true.

$2x + y = 8$	$x + 3y = 9$
$2(\mathbf{3}) + \mathbf{2} = 8$	$\mathbf{3} + 3(\mathbf{2}) = 9$
$6 + 2 = 8$	$3 + 6 = 9$
$8 = 8$	$9 = 9$

Since the ordered pair makes both equations true, the solution is (3, 2). This is a consistent system of linear equations.

Objectives: 2f

Inconsistent System

An inconsistent system has no solution. The graphs of the linear equations are parallel to each other and will not touch.

Example

Solve the following system of linear equations graphically.

$$-2x + y = 4$$
$$4x - 2y = 12$$

Write both equations in slope-intercept form, then graph them.

$-2x + y = 4$

$y = 2x + 4$

slope: 2

***y*-intercept:** 4

$4x - 2y = 12$

$-2y = -4x + 12$

$y = 2x - 6$

slope: 2

***y*-intercept:** −6

The slopes are the same, so the graph will show a pair of parallel lines.

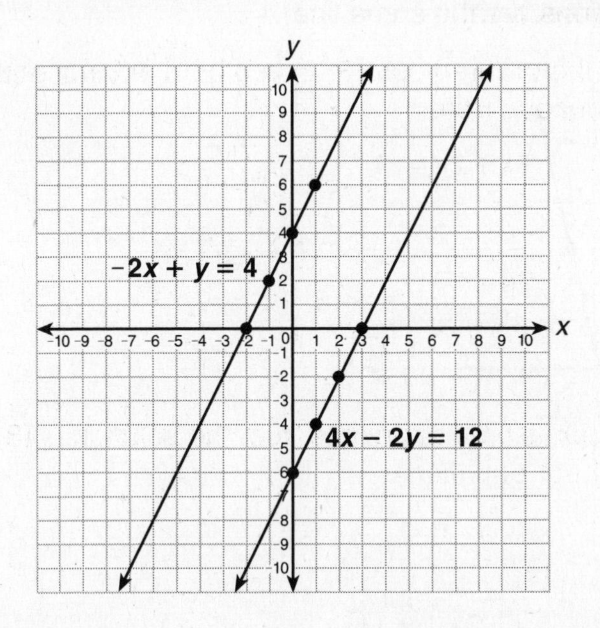

Since non-coincident parallel lines do not intersect, this system of linear equations has no solution. This is an inconsistent system of linear equations.

Dependent System

A dependent system has an infinite number of solutions. The graphs of the lines coincide, meaning that they will be exactly the same.

Example

Solve the following system of linear equations graphically.

$$-8x + 2y = -6$$
$$12x - 3y = 9$$

Write both equations in slope-intercept form, then graph them.

$$-8x + 2y = -6$$
$$2y = 8x - 6$$
$$y = 4x - 3$$

slope: 4

***y*-intercept:** −3

$$12x - 3y = 9$$
$$-3y = -12x + 9$$
$$y = 4x - 3$$

slope: 4

***y*-intercept:** −3

The slopes and the *y*-intercepts are the same, so the graph will show one line (the graphs of the equations are the same line).

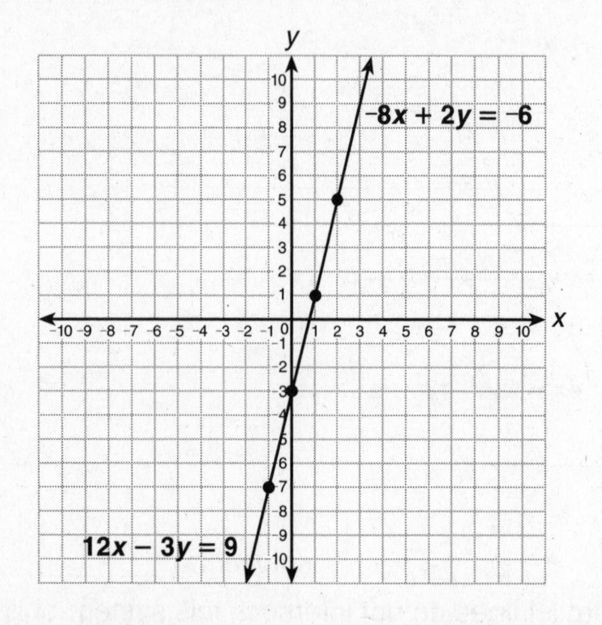

Since the graphs of the equations are the same, this system of linear equations has an infinite number of solutions. The solutions are all the ordered pairs that make either $-8x + 2y = -6$ or $12x - 3y = 9$ true. This is a dependent system of linear equations.

Practice

Directions: For Numbers 1 through 4, solve the system of linear equations graphically. Then, write the type of system for each.

1. $x - y = 2$
   $2x - 2y = 4$

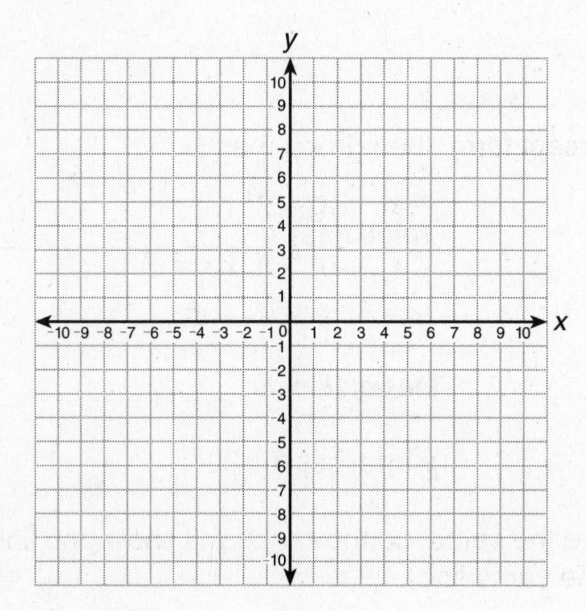

solution(s) ____________________

____

The system is ____________________.

2. $2x - 3y = 9$
   $6x - 9y = 18$

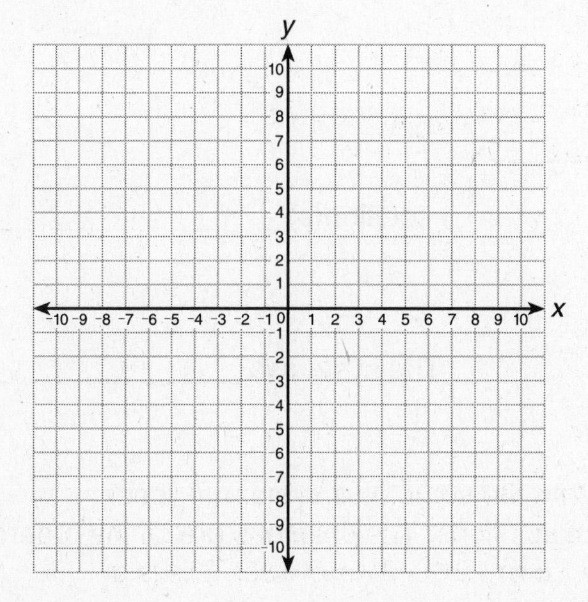

solution(s) ____________________

____

The system is ____________________.

3. $x + 2y = 2$
   $-2x + y = 1$

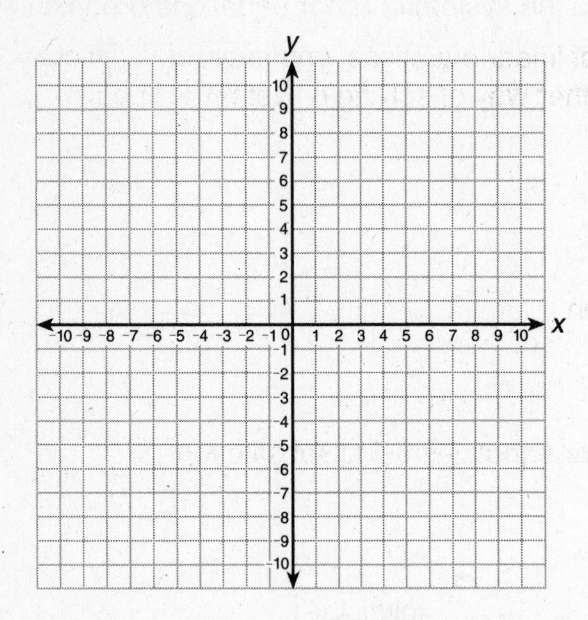

solution(s) ____________________

____

The system is ______________.

4. $x + 3y = -9$
   $4x - 3y = -6$

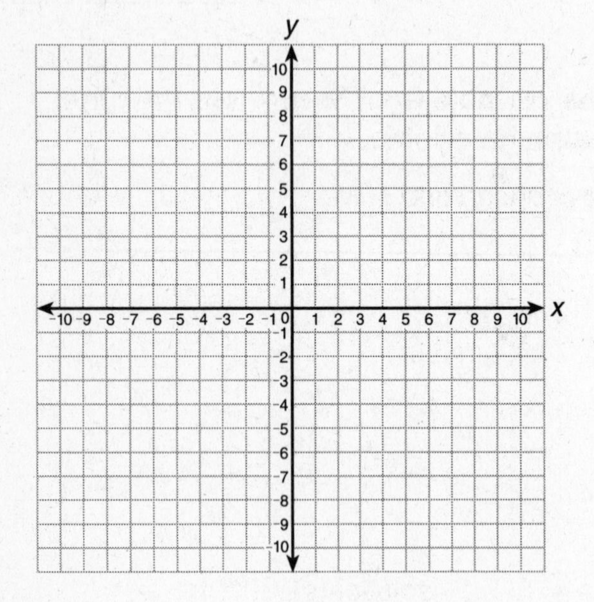

solution(s) ____________________

____

The system is ______________.

Objectives: 2f

Solving Systems of Linear Equations Using Substitution

When you use graphing to solve a system of linear equations, you may have difficulty locating the exact point of intersection. Another way of solving a system of linear equations is to use substitution.

Consistent System

A consistent system has exactly one solution.

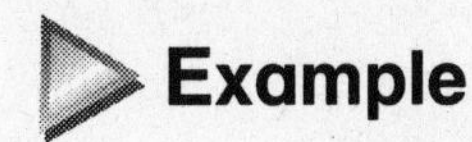

Example

Solve the following system of linear equations using substitution.

$$5x - 4y = 15$$
$$2x + 2y = 6$$

Step 1: **Solve one of the equations for one of the variables.**

$$2x + 2y = 6$$
$$2y = -2x + 6$$
$$y = -x + 3$$

Step 2: **Substitute the expression for the variable from Step 1 into the other equation and solve for the remaining variable.**

Substitute $-x + 3$ for y in the first equation and solve.

$$5x - 4y = 15$$
$$5x - 4(\mathbf{-x + 3}) = 15$$
$$5x + 4x - 12 = 15$$
$$9x = 27$$
$$x = 3$$

Step 3: **Substitute the value for the variable into one of the original equations and solve for the remaining variable.**

Substitute 3 for x in the second equation and solve.

$$2x + 2y = 6$$
$$2(\mathbf{3}) + 2y = 6$$
$$6 + 2y = 6$$
$$2y = 0$$
$$y = 0$$

Step 4: **Check the values in the original equations.**

Substitute the values of the ordered pair (3, 0) into both equations to see if they make the equations true.

$$5x - 4y = 15$$
$$5(\mathbf{3}) - 4(\mathbf{0}) = 15$$
$$15 - 0 = 15$$
$$15 = 15$$

$$2x + 2y = 6$$
$$2(\mathbf{3}) + 2(\mathbf{0}) = 6$$
$$6 + 0 = 6$$
$$6 = 6$$

Since the ordered pair makes both equations true, the solution is (3, 0). This is a consistent system of linear equations.

Sometimes, after you substitute for the first variable and simplify, the remaining variable term will disappear. You will be left with two constants separated by an equal sign. This will be the case if the system is inconsistent or dependent.

Objectives: 2f

Inconsistent System

If the equation that is left is false, the system is inconsistent and has no solution (the graphs will be parallel).

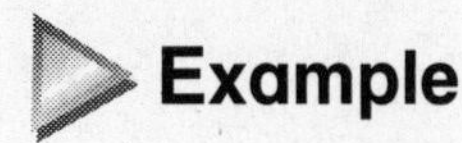

Solve the following system of linear equations using substitution.

$-8x + 6y = 12$
$4x - 3y = 21$

Solve the first equation for y.

$$-8x + 6y = 12$$

$$6y = 8x + 12$$

$$y = \frac{4}{3}x + 2$$

Substitute $\frac{4}{3}x + 2$ for y in the second equation and solve.

$$4x - 3y = 21$$

$$4x - 3\left(\frac{4}{3}\mathbf{x} + \mathbf{2}\right) = 21$$

$$4x - 4x - 6 = 21$$

$$-6 = 21$$

Since the equation is false, there is no solution. This is an inconsistent system of linear equations.

Dependent System

If the equation that is left is true, the system is dependent and has an infinite number of solutions. The solutions will be all the ordered pairs of all the points on the graph of either equation (the graphs will be the same).

Solve the following system of linear equations using substitution.

$$-2x + y = -3$$
$$4x - 2y = 6$$

Solve the first equation for y.

$$-2x + y = -3$$
$$y = 2x - 3$$

Substitute $2x - 3$ for y in the second equation and solve.

$$4x - 2y = 6$$
$$4x - 2(\mathbf{2x - 3}) = 6$$
$$4x - 4x + 6 = 6$$
$$6 = 6$$

Since the equation is true, there are an infinite number of solutions. The solutions are all the ordered pairs that make either $-2x + y = -3$ or $4x - 2y = 6$ true. This is a dependent system of linear equations.

Practice

Directions: For Numbers 1 through 6, solve the system of linear equations using substitution. Then, write the type of system for each.

1. $2x - y = 1$
   $-3x + 3y = 15$

solution(s) ________________

____

The system is ________________.

2. $2x - 3y = 6$
   $-4x + 6y = 18$

solution(s) ________________

____

The system is ________________.

3. $16x - 4y = -12$
   $x + 4y = 28$

solution(s) ________________

____

The system is ________________.

4. $4x - 2y = 3$
   $-2x + y = -7$

solution(s) ____________

____

The system is ____________.

5. $9y = 36x - 15$
   $12x - 3y = 5$

solution(s) ____________

____

The system is ____________.

6. $-2x = -3y - 13$
   $3x + y = 3$

solution(s) ____________

____

The system is ____________.

Solving Systems of Linear Equations Using Linear Combinations

The third way of solving a system of linear equations is to use **linear combinations**. To solve a system of linear equations using linear combinations, multiply one or both equations by a constant factor so that the coefficients of either x or y are additive inverses (opposites). Then, add the equations to get an equation in one variable. Next, solve for the variable and substitute that value into one of the original equations and solve for the remaining variable. In using this method, it is easier if both equations are written in standard form: $Ax + By = C$.

Consistent System

A consistent system has exactly one solution.

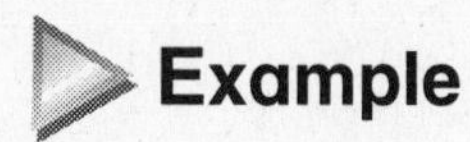

Example

Solve the following system of linear equations using linear combinations.

$$x + y = 5$$
$$x - y = 9$$

The equations are already in standard form and the coefficients of y are already additive inverses (1 and −1). If you add the equations as they appear, the y-term will drop out.

$$\begin{array}{r} x + y = 5 \\ \underline{x - y = 9} \\ 2x = 14 \end{array} \qquad \text{(The } y\text{-term dropped out; the } x\text{-term remains.)}$$

$$x = 7$$

Substitute $x = 7$ into either original equation and solve.

$$x + y = 5$$
$$\mathbf{7} + y = 5$$
$$y = -2$$

The solution looks as if it is the ordered pair (7, −2). Check the solution (7, −2) by making sure the values make both equations true.

$x + y = 5$	$x - y = 9$
$\mathbf{7} + (\mathbf{-2}) = 5$	$\mathbf{7} - (\mathbf{-2}) = 9$
$5 = 5$	$9 = 9$

Since the ordered pair makes both equations true, the solution is (7, −2). This is a consistent system of linear equations.

Here is an example in which you need to multiply one of the equations by a constant factor before you add them.

Example

Solve the following system of linear equations using linear combinations.

$$2x - y = 7$$
$$4x + 2y = 18$$

Once again, the equations are in standard form, but the coefficients of neither *x* nor *y* are additive inverses. In order for the coefficients of *y* to become additive inverses, you need to multiply both sides of the first equation by 2. Then, add the equations.

$$2(2x - y = 7) \longrightarrow \begin{array}{r} 4x - 2y = 14 \\ 4x + 2y = 18 \\ \hline 8x = 32 \\ x = 4 \end{array}$$

Substitute $x = 4$ into either original equation and solve.

$$2x - y = 7$$
$$2(4) - y = 7$$
$$8 - y = 7$$
$$-y = -1$$
$$y = 1$$

Check the solution (4, 1) by making sure the values make both equations true.

$2x - y = 7$	$4x + 2y = 18$
$2(4) - 1 = 7$	$4(4) + 2(1) = 18$
$8 - 1 = 7$	$16 + 2 = 18$
$7 = 7$	$18 = 18$

Since the ordered pair makes both equations true, the solution is (4, 1). This is a consistent system of linear equations.

Note: In solving this system of equations, you could have multiplied the first equation by -2 to make the coefficients of *x* additive inverses (-4 and 4).

Here is an example in which you need to multiply each of the equations by a constant factor before you add them.

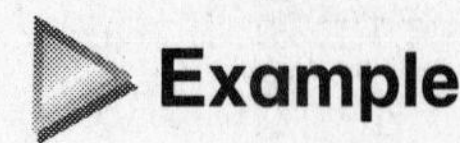

Example

Solve the following system of linear equations using linear combinations.

$$5x + 3y = -9$$
$$2x - 5y = -16$$

Multiply the first equation by 5 and the second equation by 3 to get the additive inverses of 15 and -15 as coefficients of y, then add. In this case, it may be easier to eliminate y than x because the signs of the y-terms are already opposites.

$$5(5x + 3y = -9) \longrightarrow 25x + 15y = -45$$
$$3(2x - 5y = -16) \longrightarrow 6x - 15y = -48$$
$$31x = -93$$
$$x = -3$$

Substitute $x = -3$ into either original equation and solve. It is important to use one of the original equations since there may have been a multiplication error made in creating the additive inverses. In this example, use the first equation, which shows a positive y-term (this avoids division by a negative and may make your work easier).

$$5x + 3y = -9$$
$$5(\mathbf{-3}) + 3y = -9$$
$$-15 + 3y = -9$$
$$3y = 6$$
$$y = 2$$

Check the solution $(-3, 2)$ by making sure the values make both equations true.

$$5x + 3y = -9$$
$$5(\mathbf{-3}) + 3(\mathbf{2}) = -9$$
$$-15 + 6 = -9$$
$$-9 = -9$$

$$5x + 3y = -9$$
$$2(\mathbf{-3}) - 5(\mathbf{2}) = -16$$
$$-6 - 10 = -16$$
$$-16 = -16$$

Since the ordered pair make both equations true, the solution is $(-3, 2)$. This is a consistent system of linear equations.

Inconsistent System

Just as with substitution, both variable terms may disappear when you add the equations. At that point, determine whether the resulting equation is true or false. If the equation that is left is false, the system is inconsistent and has no solution (the graphs will be parallel).

Example

Solve the following system of linear equations using linear combinations.

$$\begin{aligned} 4x + y &= 9 \\ -8x - 2y &= 7 \end{aligned}$$

Multiply the first equation by 2, then add.

$$\begin{array}{r} 8x + 2y = 18 \\ \underline{-8x - 2y = \ \ 7} \\ 0 = 25 \end{array}$$

Since both variable terms disappeared, and the resulting equation is false, there is no solution. This is an inconsistent system of linear equations.

Dependent System

If the equation that is left is true, the system is dependent and has an infinite number of solutions. The solutions will be all the ordered pairs of all the points on the graph of either equation (the graphs will be the same).

Example

Solve the following system of linear equations using linear combinations.

$$\begin{aligned} 2x - y &= 4 \\ 6x - 3y &= 12 \end{aligned}$$

Multiply the first equation by −3, then add.

$$\begin{array}{r} -6x + 3y = -12 \\ \underline{6x - 3y = \ \ 12} \\ 0 = 0 \end{array}$$

Since both variable terms disappeared, and the resulting equation is true, there are an infinite number of solutions. The solutions are all the ordered pairs that make either $2x - y = 4$ or $6x - 3y = 12$ true. This is a dependent system of linear equations.

Practice

Directions: For Numbers 1 through 6, solve the system of linear equations using linear combinations. Then, write the type of system for each.

1. $6x - y = -11$
   $-7x + 5y = 32$

solution(s) ________________

____

The system is ______________.

2. $x - 2y = 6$
   $-2x + 9y = -22$

solution(s) ________________

____

The system is ______________.

3. $6x + 2y = 8$
   $-12x - 4y = -16$

solution(s) ________________

____

The system is ______________.

4. $4x + y = 23$
   $-3x - y = -19$

solution(s) ________________

____

The system is ________________.

5. $-2x + 5y = -15$
   $4x - 3y = 9$

solution(s) ________________

____

The system is ________________.

6. $2x - y = -3$
   $-6x + 3y = 12$

solution(s) ________________

____

The system is ________________.

Objectives: 2f

Systems of Linear Equations Applications

There are many practical uses for systems of linear equations.

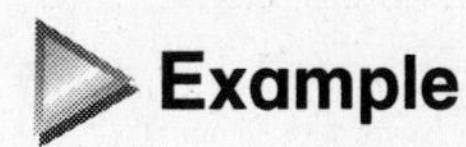

Example

Mr. Yablonsky purchased tickets to the Jackson Zoo for a total of 23 people. Adult tickets cost $11 per person and child tickets cost $7 per person. Mr. Yablonsky spent a total of $181 on zoo tickets. How many adult tickets and how many child tickets did Mr. Yablonsky purchase?

Set up the system of linear equations that represents the information. Let a = the number of adult tickets and c = the number of child tickets.

$a + c = 23$ (Mr. Yablonsky bought a total of 23 adult and child tickets.)

$11a + 7c = 181$ (The cost for adult tickets + the cost for child tickets = $181.)

Use graphing, substitution, or elimination to solve the system of linear equations. Since the coefficients of a and c in the first equation are both 1, use substitution. Solve the first equation for a.

$$a = 23 - c$$

Substitute $23 - c$ for a in the second equation and solve for c.

$$11a + 7c = 181$$
$$11(\mathbf{23 - c}) + 7c = 181$$
$$253 - 11c + 7c = 181$$
$$253 - 4c = 181$$
$$-4c = -72$$
$$c = 18$$

Now substitute 18 for c in either original equation and solve for a.

$$a + c = 23$$
$$a + \mathbf{18} = 23$$
$$a = 5$$

Check the values of the ordered pair (5, 18) by making sure they are solutions to both original equations.

$a + c = 23$	$11a + 7c = 181$
$\mathbf{5} + \mathbf{18} = 23$	$11(\mathbf{5}) + 7(\mathbf{18}) = 181$
$23 = 23$	$55 + 126 = 181$
	$181 = 181$

Since the values of the ordered pair make both equations true, the solution is (5, 18).

Mr. Yablonsky purchased 5 adult tickets and 18 child tickets to the Jackson Zoo.

Here is the graph of this system of linear equations. Since the number of adult tickets and the number of child tickets must be positive or zero, only Quadrant I is shown in the graph.

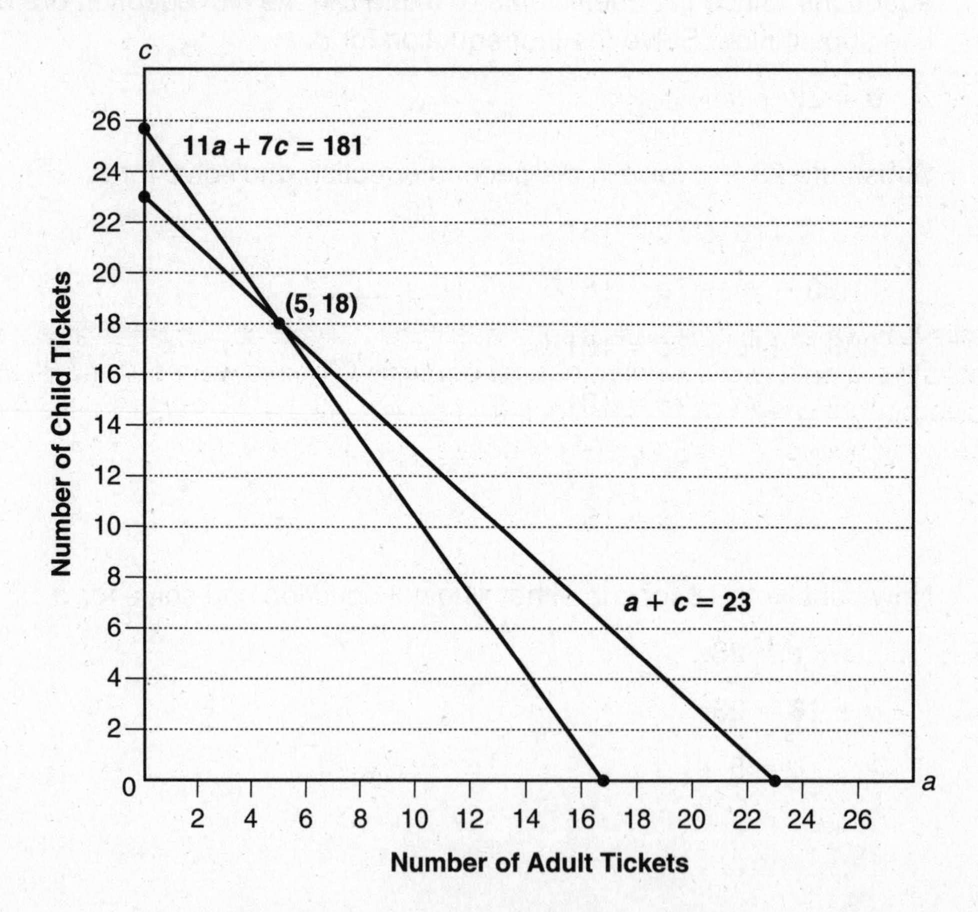

Notice that the graphs intersect at the point (5, 18) where the first coordinate represents the value of *a* (horizontal axis), and the second coordinate represents the value of *c* (vertical axis).

Practice

Directions: For Numbers 1 and 2, set up a system of linear equations to represent each situation. Then, use either graphing, substitution, or linear combinations to solve the system of linear equations and answer the questions.

1. Hector has a number of baseballs that all have the same mass and a number of softballs that all have the same mass. He found the mass of 3 baseballs and 9 softballs to be 78 ounces. Hector also found the mass of 6 baseballs and 4 softballs to be 58 ounces. What is the mass of each baseball, b, and each softball, s?

2. Sallie bought some hardback books and some paperback books. All hardback books were sold for $18 each, and all paperback books were sold for $12 each. Sallie bought a total of 17 hardback and paperback books for $228. How many hardback books, h, and paperback books, p, did Sallie buy?

Solving Systems of Linear Inequalities Graphically

To solve systems of linear inequalities, graph the linear inequalities and shade the correct region of the graph.

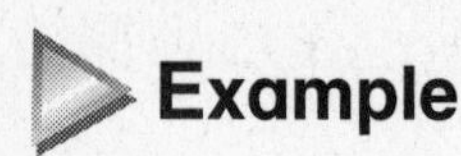

Example

Solve the following system of linear inequalities by graphing.

$2x + 3y < 6$
$4x - 2y \geq 8$

Step 1: **Replace the inequality symbols with equal signs.**

$2x + 3y < 6$ $\quad$ $4x - 2y \geq 8$

$2x + 3y = 6$ $\quad$ $4x - 2y = 8$

Step 2: **Write each equation in slope-intercept form.**

$2x + 3y = 6$ $\quad$ $4x - 2y = 8$

$3y = -2x + 6$ $\quad$ $-2y = -4x + 8$

$y = -\frac{2}{3}x + 2$ $\quad$ $y = 2x - 4$

slope: $-\frac{2}{3}$ $\quad$ **slope:** 2

***y*-intercept:** 2 $\quad$ ***y*-intercept:** -4

Step 3: **Plot each *y*-intercept; find a few other points and draw each boundary line.** Use a dashed line if $>$ or $<$. Use a solid line if $\geq$ or $\leq$.

Step 4: **Select a test point for each inequality.** An easy point to use is (0, 0).

Substitute the values of the test point (0, 0) into both original inequalities to see if they make the inequalities true.

$2x + 3y < 6$ $\quad$ $4x - 2y \geq 8$

$2(\mathbf{0}) + 3(\mathbf{0}) < 6$ $\quad$ $4(\mathbf{0}) - 2(\mathbf{0}) \geq 8$

$0 + 0 < 6$ $\quad$ $0 - 0 \geq 8$

$0 < 6$ $\quad$ $0 \geq 8$

The values of the test point make one of the inequalities true and the other false.

Step 5: **Shade the side of the boundary line that satisfies each inequality.**

If the test point makes the inequality true, shade the side of the boundary line where the test point is located.

If the test point makes the inequality false, shade the side of the boundary line opposite the test point.

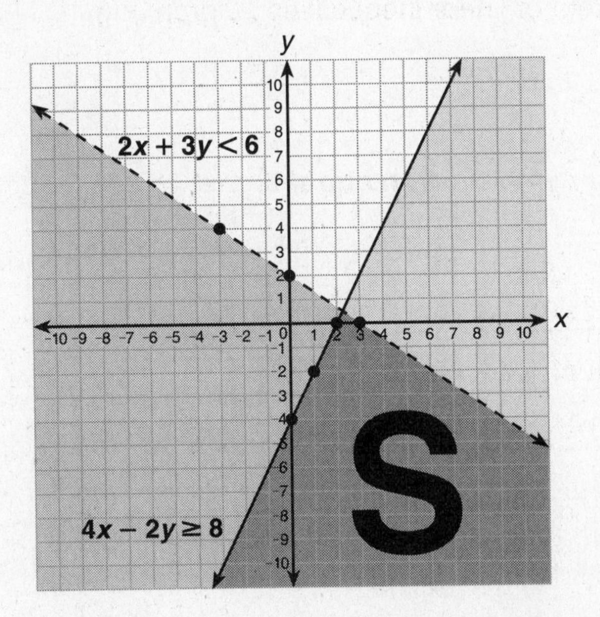

The solution to the system of linear inequalities is the set of ordered pairs that makes both of the inequalities true. The points of these ordered pairs are in the region on the coordinate plane where the graphs of each inequality intersect, indicated by **S**.

Practice

Directions: For Numbers 1 through 4, solve each system of linear inequalities graphically.

1. $x + 2y \leq 6$
   $y > 2x - 4$

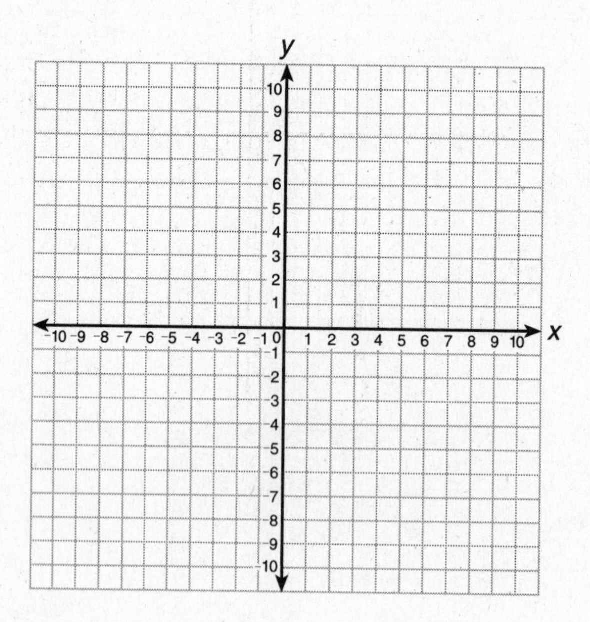

2. $y > x + 1$
   $y \geq 3x + 2$

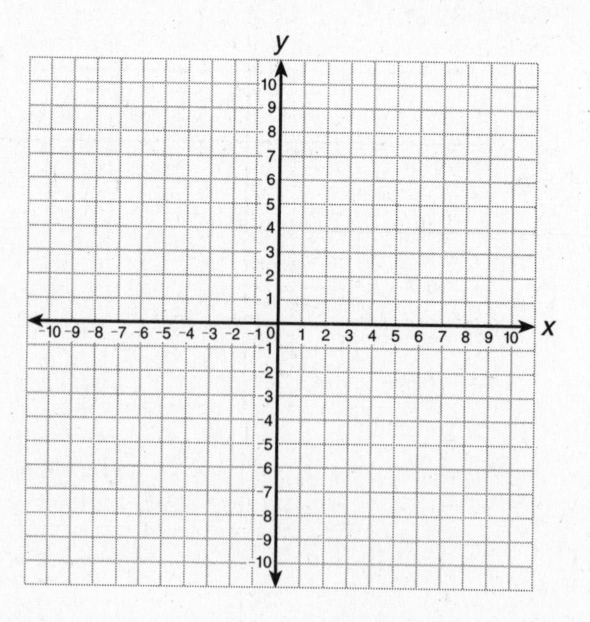

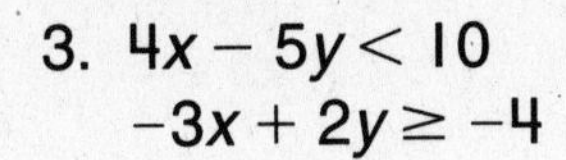

3. $4x - 5y < 10$
   $-3x + 2y \geq -4$

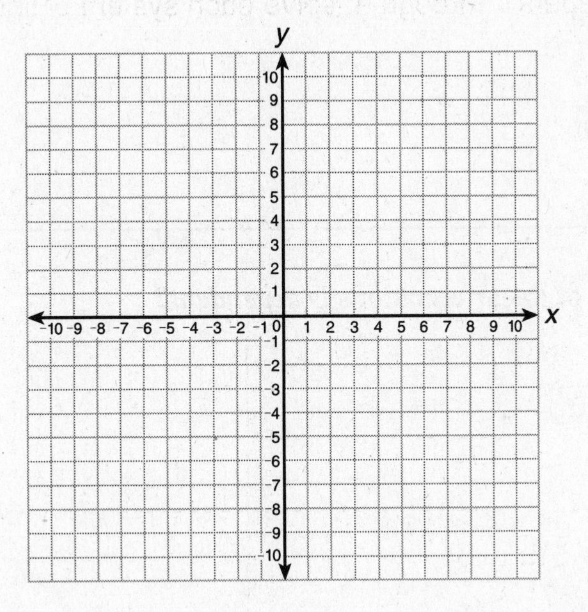

4. $x \geq 0$
   $y \geq 0$

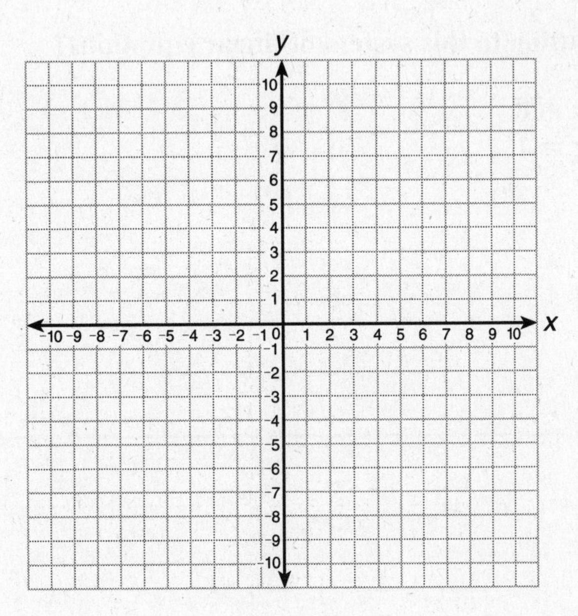

SATP Practice begins on the following page.

1. **What type of system is the following system of linear equations?**

$$x + y = 6$$
$$2x + y = 6$$

A Independent

B Dependent

C Inconsistent

D Consistent

---

2. **Which system of linear equations is *dependent*?**

F $x + y = 3$
$2x + 2y = 4$

G $2x + y = 1$
$3x + 6y = -1$

H $3x - y = 7$
$-3x + y = -7$

J $x = 3$
$x + 2y = 3$

---

3. **What is the solution to this system of linear equations?**

$$2x + y = 8$$
$$x - 3y = 4$$

A $(-4, -1)$

B $(-2, -4)$

C $(4, 0)$

D $(2, 1)$

---

4. **How many solutions does the following system of linear equations have?**

$$-3y = 2x - 9$$
$$4x + 6y = 15$$

F None

G One

H Two

J Infinite

---

5. **Which graph shows the solution to the following system of linear inequalities?**

$$x + y \leq 5$$
$$2y \geq 2x - 6$$

A

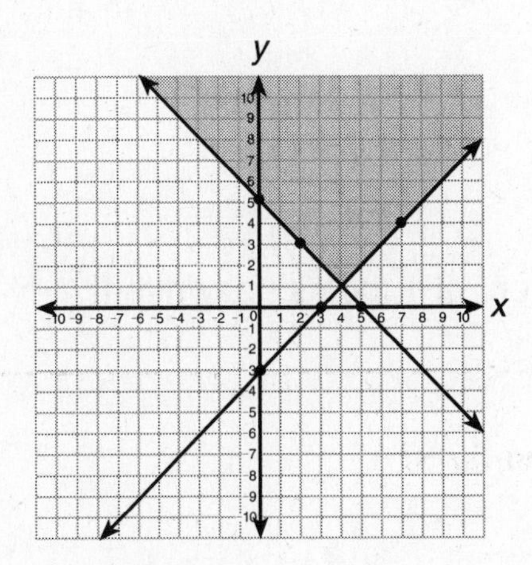

C

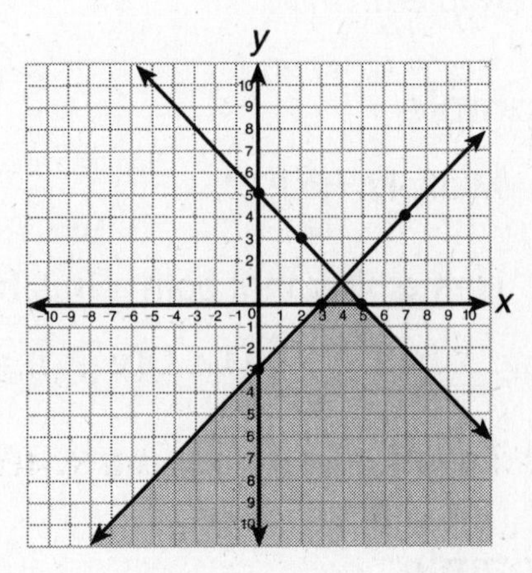

B

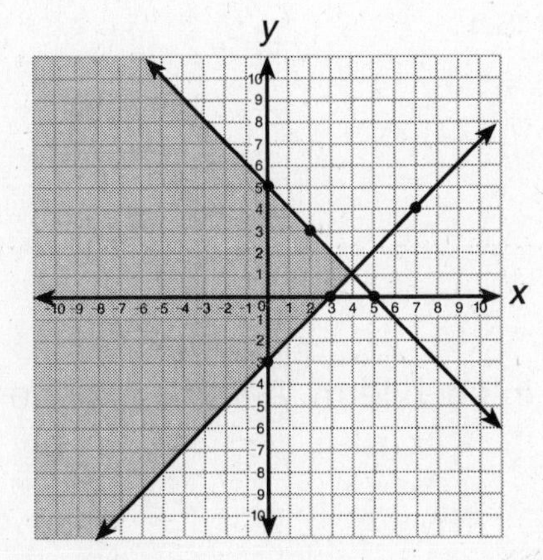

D

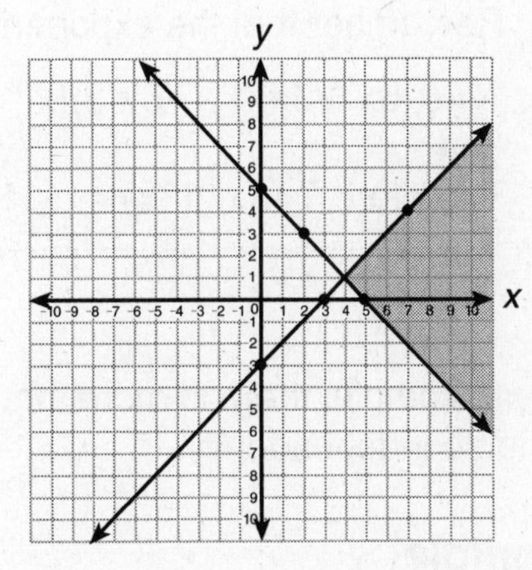

Objectives: 1a, 2g

Lesson 6: Operations on Polynomials

In this lesson, you will add, subtract, multiply, and divide polynomials.

Monomials

A **monomial** is a constant, a variable, or the product of one or more constants and one or more variables.

Multiplying Monomials

When multiplying monomials, multiply the coefficients and add the exponents of the like bases (variables).

Example

Multiply: $(y^7)(y^4)$

Remember that both terms have a coefficient of 1 that is not written.

$$(y^7)(y^4) = (1 \bullet 1)(y^{7+4}) = y^{11}$$

Therefore, $(y^7)(y^4) = y^{11}$.

Example

Multiply: $(-5x^4)(3x)$

Remember that the exponent of the x in $3x$ is 1.

$$(-5x^4)(3x) = (-5 \bullet 3)(x^{4+1}) = -15x^5$$

Therefore, $(-5x^4)(3x) = -15x^5$.

In the next example, there is more than one variable in each term. Add the exponents of each variable independently.

Example

Multiply: $(2a^3b^3d^2)(13a^3b^2c^6)$

$$(2a^3b^3d^2)(13a^3b^2c^6) = (2 \bullet 13)(a^{3+3})(b^{3+2})(c^6)(d^2) = 26a^6b^5c^6d^2$$

Therefore, $(2a^3b^3d^2)(13a^3b^2c^6) = 26a^6b^5c^6d^2$.

Objectives: 1a, 2g DOK 1

Practice

Directions: For Numbers 1 through 8, multiply the monomials.

1. $(3a^4b^5)(4a^2b^3)$

2. $(-3xy)(-3xy)$

3. $(16g^4h^3i^8)(3g^2hi^4)$

4. $(-3x^4y^3z^2)(4y^5)$

5. $(a^3b^2)(60a^4b^3)$

6. $(12m^3n^3)(2m^{10}n^4)$

7. $(5a^3b^7c^9)(-5ab^2c^3d)$

8. $(-3fgh)(2f^{34})$

Dividing Monomials

When dividing monomials, write the coefficients in simplest form and subtract the exponents (larger – smaller) of the like bases (variables). Write the base and its new exponent in the numerator or denominator, wherever the larger exponent originally was. (In the examples below, the bases with the larger exponents are shown in bold-faced type.)

Example

Divide: $\frac{12x^3y^7z}{9x^3y^3z^2}$

Remember, if you don't see an exponent on a variable, then the exponent is a 1.

$$\frac{12x^3\mathbf{y^7}z}{9x^3y^3\mathbf{z^2}} = \frac{12}{9} \bullet \frac{x^{3-3}y^{7-3}}{z^{2-1}} = \frac{12y^4}{9z} = \frac{4y^4}{3z}$$

Therefore, $\frac{12x^3y^7z}{9x^3y^3z^2} = \frac{4y^4}{3z}$.

If all the bases with the higher exponents are in the numerator or denominator, write a 1 where the bases with the lower exponents were.

Example

Divide: $\frac{2a^4b^5}{6a^7b^9}$

$$\frac{2a^4b^5}{6\mathbf{a^7b^9}} = \frac{2}{6} \bullet \frac{1}{a^{7-4}b^{9-5}} = \frac{2}{6a^3b^4} = \frac{1}{3a^3b^4}$$

Therefore, $\frac{2a^4b^5}{6a^7b^9} = \frac{1}{3a^3b^4}$.

Example

Divide: $\frac{2x^6y^{11}z}{x^5y^{10}}$

$$\frac{2\mathbf{x^6y^{11}z}}{x^5y^{10}} = \frac{2}{1} \bullet \frac{x^{6-5}y^{11-10}z}{1} = \frac{2xyz}{1} = 2xyz$$

Therefore, $\frac{2x^6y^{11}z}{x^5y^{10}} = 2xyz$.

Practice

Directions: For Numbers 1 through 8, divide the monomials.

1. $\frac{2x^4y^4z^4}{x^2y^3z^4}$

2. $\frac{5a^3b^7c^2}{15a^7b^3c^4}$

3. $\frac{13p^5q^7}{27p^7q^3r}$

4. $\frac{8a^3b^4}{-12a^5b^2}$

5. $\frac{18x^2y^8}{27x^4y^3z}$

6. $\frac{-19a^2b^6c^8d}{38a^5b^4c^4d^2}$

7. $\frac{-f^6g^3h}{-4f^7gh^3}$

8. $\frac{2x^4y^4z^4}{4x^2y^3z^4}$

Monomials Raised to a Power

When raising a monomial to a power, raise the coefficient to the power and multiply each exponent by the power.

Example

Simplify: $(j^6k^2l^3)^4$

Remember, when you raise a 1 to any power, it equals 1.

$$(j^6k^2l^3)^4 = 1^4(j^{6 \cdot 4})(k^{2 \cdot 4})(l^{3 \cdot 4}) = j^{24}k^8l^{12}$$

Therefore, $(j^6k^2l^3)^4 = j^{24}k^8l^{12}$.

Example

Simplify: $(7ab^5)^2$

Remember, if you don't see an exponent on a variable, it is a 1.

$$(7ab^5)^2 = 7^2(a^{1 \cdot 2})(b^{5 \cdot 2}) = 49a^2b^{10}$$

Therefore, $(7ab^5)^2 = 49a^2b^{10}$.

Any negative coefficient raised to an even power is positive. Any negative coefficient raised to an odd power is negative.

Example

Simplify: $(-3x^2y^5)^4$

$$(-3x^2y^5)^4 = (-3)^4(x^{2 \cdot 4})(y^{5 \cdot 4}) = 81x^8y^{20}$$

Therefore, $(-3x^2y^5)^4 = 81x^8y^{20}$.

Example

Simplify: $(-4d^2e^3)^5$

$$(-4d^2e^3)^5 = (-4)^5(d^{2 \cdot 5})(e^{3 \cdot 5}) = -1{,}024d^{10}e^{15}$$

Therefore, $(-4d^2e^3)^5 = -1{,}024d^{10}e^{15}$.

Practice

Directions: For Numbers 1 through 8, simplify each monomial raised to a power.

1. $(6a^4g^2)^3$

2. $(-5x^4y)^6$

3. $(-9f^7g^5h^4)^3$

4. $(-7w)^4$

5. $(8x^5y^7z^6)^4$

6. $\left(\frac{1}{3}v^5w^8\right)^4$

7. $(r^7s^2t)^6$

8. $\left(-\frac{2}{5}j^2k^6l^3\right)^4$

Monomials with Negative Exponents

When simplifying a monomial with a negative exponent, the monomial equals its reciprocal with a positive exponent.

$x^{-5} = \frac{1}{x^5}$ and $\frac{1}{x^{-3}} = x^3$

Example

Simplify: 7^{-3}

$$7^{-3} = \frac{1}{7^3} = \frac{1}{343}$$

Therefore, $7^{-3} = \frac{1}{343}$.

When simplifying a monomial with variables that have negative exponents, rewrite the monomial using only positive exponents on the variables.

Example

Simplify: $4x^2y^{-6}z^{-8}$

$$4x^2y^{-6}z^{-8} = (4)(x^2)(y^{-6})(z^{-8}) = (4)(x^2)\left(\frac{1}{y^6}\right)\left(\frac{1}{z^8}\right) = \frac{4x^2}{y^6z^8}$$

Therefore, $4x^2y^{-6}z^{-8} = \frac{4x^2}{y^6z^8}$.

The previous monomial rules for multiplying, dividing, and raising to a power still hold for monomials with negative exponents. Be sure to rewrite the answers so that they do not include any negative exponents.

Example

Multiply: $(4a^3b^{-1})(-5a^{-6}b)$

$$(4a^3b^{-1})(-5a^{-6}b) = [4 \cdot (-5)][a^{3 + (-6)}](b^{-1 + 1}) = -20a^{-3} = -\frac{20}{a^3}$$

Therefore, $(4a^3b^{-1})(-5a^{-6}b) = -\frac{20}{a^3}$.

Example

Simplify: $(3x^2y^{-4})^{-4}$

$$(3x^2y^{-4})^{-4} = 3^{-4}[x^{2 \cdot (-4)}][y^{-4 \cdot (-4)}] = \frac{1}{81}x^{-8}y^{16} = \frac{y^{16}}{81x^8}$$

Therefore, $(3x^2y^{-4})^{-4} = \frac{y^{16}}{81x^8}$.

 Practice

Directions: For Numbers 1 through 8, simplify, multiply, or divide. Be sure your answers do not include any negative exponents.

1. $(3^{-5})(3^{9})$

2. $[(-4)^{-3}][(-4)^{-5}]$

3. $4a^{-3}b^{5}c^{-6}de^{-1}$

4. $(3h^{2}j^{-5}k^{-3})(-6h^{4}j^{-3}k^{7})$

5. $(-8x^{-4}y^{2}z^{-9})(-x^{7}y^{2}z^{-3})$

6. $\frac{9a^{7}b^{-4}c^{-9}d^{-1}}{-3a^{-7}b^{3}c^{-3}}$

7. $(6m^{-4}n^{7})^{-5}$

8. $(-4w^{-3}x^{5}y^{-7}z^{3})^{3}$

Square Roots

A perfect square monomial has a perfect square coefficient and even exponents on every variable. The monomials $4x^2$, $16b^6$, and $25m^{12}$ are perfect squares.

To simplify the square root $(\sqrt{\ })$ of a monomial, find the square root of the coefficient and divide the exponent(s) of the variable(s) by 2. Remember that each perfect square has two roots, one positive and one negative. Perfect square monomials will also have two roots. Use the principal (positive) root when stating your answer.

Example

Simplify: $\sqrt{16x^6y^2}$

How do you know that this monomial is a perfect square? Its coefficient, 16, is a perfect square. In addition, the exponents on every variable are even.

$$\sqrt{16x^6y^2} = \sqrt{4^2x^{(2 \cdot 3)}y^{(2 \cdot 1)}} = 4x^3y$$

Therefore, $\sqrt{16x^6y^2} = 4x^3y$.

Example

Simplify: $\sqrt{w^4x^8y^{12}z^6}$

The coefficient is a 1, which is a perfect square with a square root of 1.

$$\sqrt{w^4x^8y^{12}z^6} = \sqrt{1^2w^{(2 \cdot 2)}x^{(2 \cdot 4)}y^{(2 \cdot 6)}z^{(2 \cdot 3)}} = w^2x^4y^6z^3$$

Therefore, $\sqrt{w^4x^8y^{12}z^6} = w^2x^4y^6z^3$.

Example

Simplify: $\sqrt{\frac{4}{9}a^4b^6}$

The coefficient in this example is a fraction. A fraction is a perfect square if both the numerator and denominator are perfect squares. In this case, $\frac{4}{9}$ is a perfect square since both 4 and 9 are perfect squares.

$$\sqrt{\frac{4}{9}a^4b^6} = \sqrt{\left(\frac{2}{3}\right)^2 a^{(2 \cdot 2)}b^{(2 \cdot 3)}} = \frac{2}{3}a^2b^3 = \frac{2a^2b^3}{3}$$

Therefore, $\sqrt{\frac{4}{9}a^4b^6} = \frac{2a^2b^3}{3}$.

Objectives: 1a, 2g **DOK 1**

Practice

Directions: For Numbers 1 through 8, write the principal square root of each monomial.

1. $\sqrt{a^2b^{10}c^8}$

2. $\sqrt{64x^8}$

3. $\sqrt{0.16r^6s^4t^{16}}$

4. $\sqrt{121x^{14}y^{26}z^4}$

5. $\sqrt{100j^8k^{18}}$

6. $\sqrt{\frac{1}{4}z^6}$

7. $\sqrt{49f^6g^8h^2}$

8. $\sqrt{\frac{25}{81}a^2b^{10}}$

Polynomials

A **polynomial** is a monomial or the sum of monomials. Each monomial of a polynomial is called a **term** of the polynomial. A polynomial with two terms is called a **binomial**. A polynomial with three terms is called a **trinomial**. The terms of a polynomial are usually written in **standard form:** decreasing order of the exponents of the variable or of one of the variables. The **degree of a term** of a polynomial is the sum of each exponent of each variable of that term. The **degree of the polynomial** is the highest degree of the individual terms of that polynomial. For example, the degrees of the terms of $4x^3y^2 + 2x^2y^4 - xy^8$ are 5, 6, and 9. The degree of the polynomial is 9.

Adding Polynomials

To add polynomials, add the like terms of the polynomials.

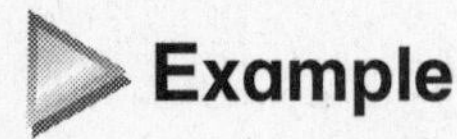

Example

Add: $(4a^3 - 9a^2 + 3a) + (11a^3 - 4a)$

The like terms are the a^3- and a-terms. There is only one a^2-term, so it will stay the same.

$$(4a^3 - 9a^2 + 3a) + (11a^3 - 4a) = (4 + 11)a^3 - 9a^2 + [3 + (-4)]a$$
$$= 15a^3 - 9a^2 - a$$

Therefore, $(4a^3 - 9a^2 + 3a) + (11a^3 - 4a) = 15a^3 - 9a^2 - a$.

Subtracting Polynomials

To subtract polynomials, add the opposite. Change the $-$ to $+$ and every term in the second polynomial to its opposite, then follow the rule for addition.

Example

Subtract: $(x^2 + 11x - 4) - (3x^2 - 7)$

Change $-$ to $+$ and change each term of $3x^2 - 7$ to its opposite. Then add.

$$(x^2 + 11x - 4) - (3x^2 - 7) = (x^2 + 11x - 4) + (-3x^2 + 7)$$
$$= -2x^2 + 11x + 3$$

Therefore, $(x^2 + 11x - 4) - (3x^2 - 7) = -2x^2 + 11x + 3$.

Objectives: 1a, 2g

Adding and Subtracting Polynomials Using Algebraic Tiles

Some algebraic procedures might be easier to understand when you apply geometric concepts to create a model for the problem. These algebraic tiles represent algebraic expressions and real numbers. Shaded tiles indicate negative algebraic expressions and real numbers. Algebraic tiles can be used to show addition and subtraction of polynomials.

This tile is 1 unit by 1 unit. The tile represents 1:

1

This tile is 1 unit by x units. The tile represents x:

x

This tile is x units by x units. The tile represents x^2:

x^2

This tile is 1 unit by 1 unit. The tile represents -1:

This tile is 1 unit by x units. The tile represents $-x$:

$-x$

This tile is x units by x units. The tile represents $-x^2$:

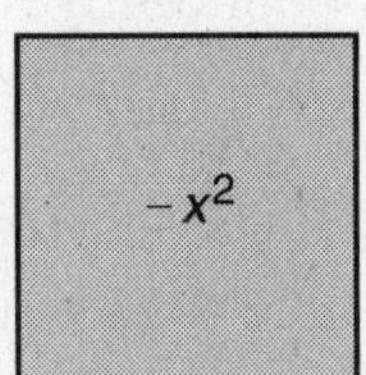

Addition

Combine the like terms. Remember that opposite terms add to zero.

Example

Add: $(3y^2 - 4y + 2) + (-y^2 + 2y + 3)$

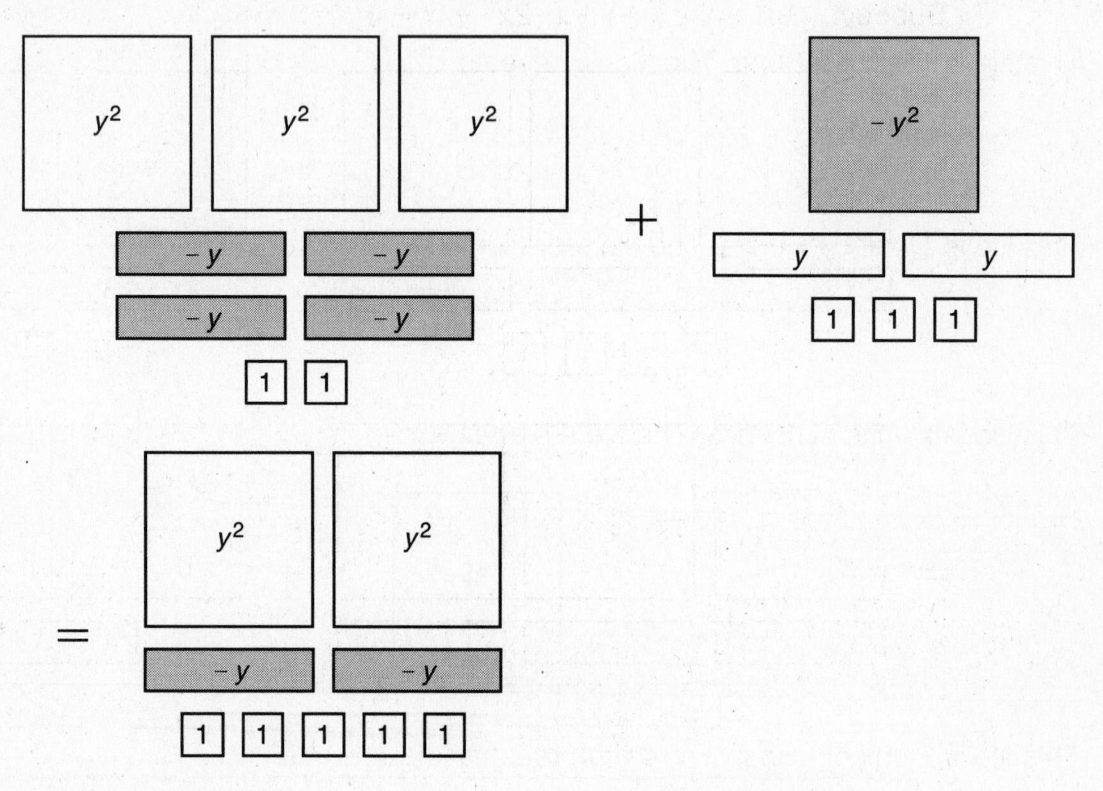

Therefore, $(3y^2 - 4y + 2) + (-y^2 + 2y + 3) = 2y^2 - 2y + 5$.

Objectives: 1a, 2g

Subtraction

Add the opposite. Change − to + and each term of the second polynomial to its opposite. Then add.

Example

Subtract: $(3x^2 - 3x + 4) - (-2x^2 + x + 3)$

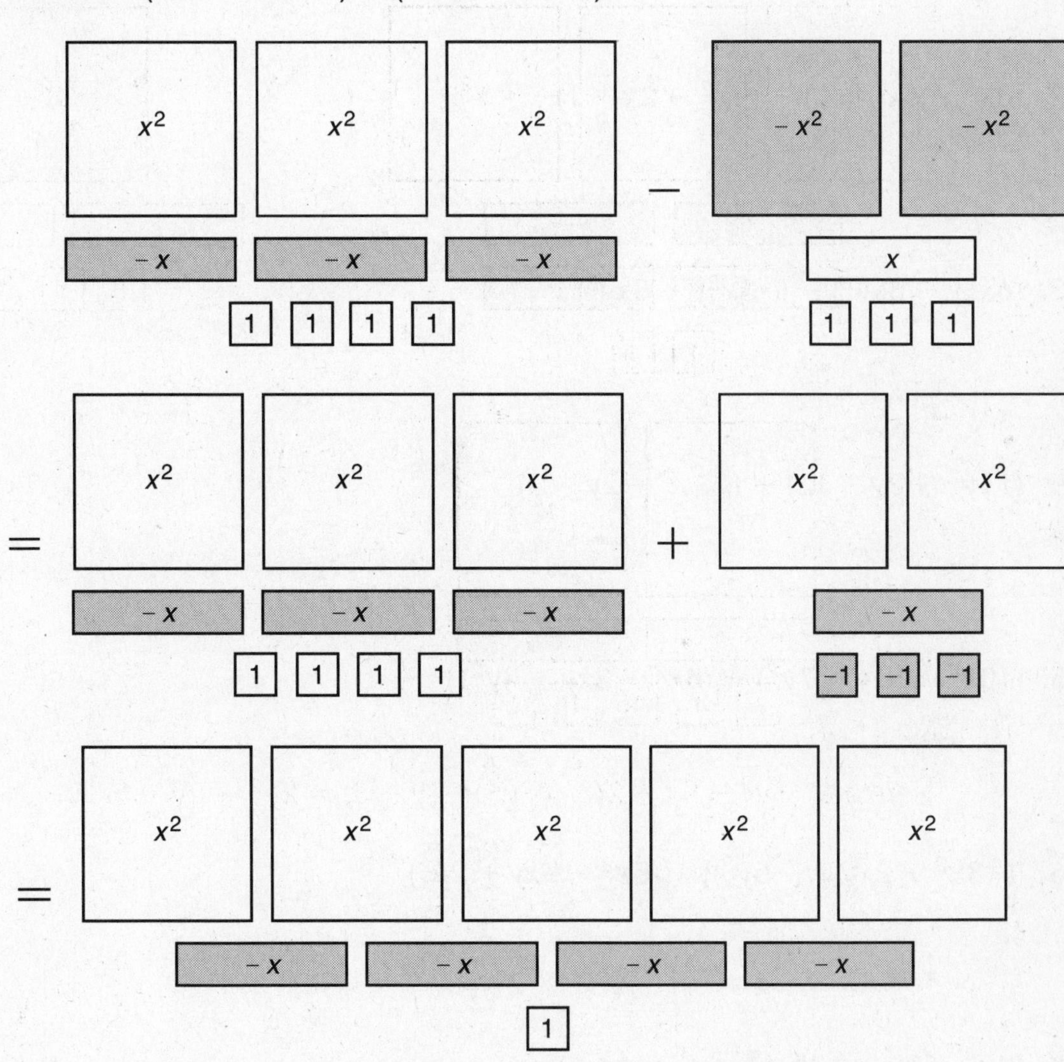

Therefore, $(3x^2 - 3x + 4) - (-2x^2 + x + 3) = 5x^2 - 4x + 1$.

Practice

Directions: For Numbers 1 through 8, add or subtract the polynomials.

1. $(8xy^3 + 3x^3y) + (-6xy^3 + x^3y)$

2. $(8x^3 - 6x^2 + 3) - (4x^2 - 2x + 1)$

3. $(6x^2y - 3xy^2) - (-3x^2y + 5xy^2)$

4. $(11y^2 - 3y + 12) + (-3y^2 - 2y - 7)$

5. $(10x^2 - 5xy + 7y^2) - (5x^2 + 3xy + 4y^2)$

6. $[(-3x^2 + 2xy + (-5y^2)] + (5x^2 - 4xy + 2y^2)$

7. $(4x^4 + 3x^3y - 4xy^3) + (-5x^4 - 9x^2y^2 + 3y^4)$

8. $(3x^3 - 2xy^3 + 3xy^4) - (x^3 + 3xy^3 + xy^4)$

Objectives: 1a, 2g

Multiplying Polynomials

To multiply polynomials, use a form of the distributive property. Multiply each term of the first polynomial by each term of the second polynomial, then combine the like terms when appropriate. When multiplying two binomials, you can use the acronym FOIL (First, Outer, Inner, Last) to help you multiply.

Example

Multiply: $5w(7w^2 - 8w + 3)$

Multiply $5w$ by each term of $7w^2 - 8w + 3$.

$$5w(7w^2 - 8w + 3) = (5w \bullet 7w^2) - (5w \bullet 8w) + (5w \bullet 3)$$
$$= 35w^3 - 40w^2 + 15w$$

Therefore, $5w(7w^2 - 8w + 3) = 35w^3 - 40w^2 + 15w$.

Example

Multiply: $(x - 5)(2x + 3)$

Use the acronym FOIL to multiply the binomials.

$$(x - 5)(2x + 3) = 2x^2 + 3x - 10x - 15$$
$$= 2x^2 - 7x - 15$$

Therefore, $(x - 5)(2x + 3) = 2x^2 - 7x - 15$.

Example

Multiply: $(3x + 4)(4x^2 - 6x + 2)$

Multiply $3x$ by each term of $4x^2 - 6x + 2$. Then, multiply $+4$ by each term of $4x^2 - 6x + 2$. Finally, combine the like terms.

$$(3x + 4)(4x^2 - 6x + 2) = 12x^3 - 18x^2 + 6x + 16x^2 - 24x + 8$$
$$= 12x^3 - 2x^2 - 18x + 8$$

Therefore, $(3x + 4)(4x^2 - 6x + 2) = 12x^3 - 2x^2 - 18x + 8$.

Dividing Polynomials

To divide polynomials, use a process similar to long division of real numbers. As with place value in real numbers, make sure you keep the terms lined up.

Example

Divide: $(6x^3 - 2x^2 + 8x) \div 2x$

Set up the division similar to long division of a three-digit real number by a one-digit real number.

$$\begin{array}{r|l} & 3x^2 - x + 4 \\ 2x & 6x^3 - 2x^2 + 8x \\ & -(6x^3) \\ & \quad -2x^2 \\ & \quad -(-2x^2) \\ & \qquad 8x \\ & \qquad -8x \\ & \qquad 0 \end{array}$$

Therefore, $(6x^3 - 2x^2 + 8x) \div 2x = 3x^2 - x + 4$.

Example

Divide: $(2x^2 + x - 15) \div (x + 3)$

Set it up as a long division problem.

$$\begin{array}{r|l} & 2x - 5 \\ x + 3 & 2x^2 + x - 15 \\ & -(2x^2 + 6x) \\ & \quad -5x - 15 \\ & \quad -(-5x - 15) \\ & \qquad 0 \end{array}$$

Therefore, $(2x^2 + x - 15) \div (x + 3) = 2x - 5$.

Objectives: 1a, 2g

Multiplying and Dividing Polynomials Using Algebraic Tiles

Algebraic tiles can also be used to show multiplication and division of some polynomials. Multiplication must be between two monomials, two binomials, or a monomial and a binomial. Each must have at most one variable, and each variable must have a greatest degree of 1 (the greatest exponent on any term is 1). Division must be a trinomial divided by a binomial, a binomial divided by either a binomial or a monomial, or a monomial divided by a monomial, each with at most one variable. The polynomial being divided (the dividend) can be of at most degree 2. The polynomial doing the dividing can be of at most degree 1.

Multiplication

Multiplication can be shown as the area of a rectangular array of tiles. The sides of the rectangle have lengths that correspond to each factor.

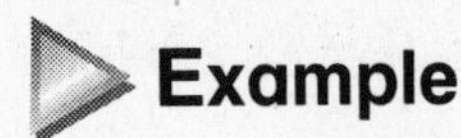

Example

Multiply: $(2x + 1)(2x + 3)$

Create a rectangle whose side lengths represent $2x + 1$ and $2x + 3$.

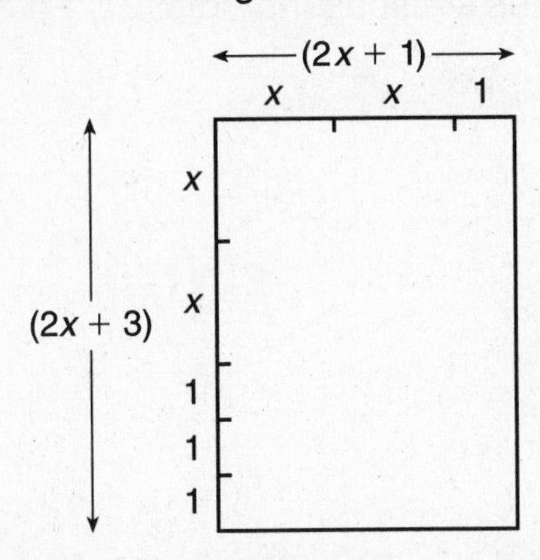

Divide the rectangle into smaller sections by drawing in partitions for each value of x and 1. Label each of these sections by multiplying the dimensions of the section (shade where necessary). Then, combine the like terms to find the product.

	x	x	1
x	x^2	x^2	x
x	x^2	x^2	x
1	x	x	1
1	x	x	1
1	x	x	1

Therefore, $(2x + 1)(2x + 3) = 4x^2 + 8x + 3$.

Division

Because division is the opposite of multiplication, it can also be shown using a rectangular array of tiles. Use the divisor as the length of one side of the rectangle. Then, finish the rectangle to correspond to the dividend. The quotient will be the other dimension of the array.

Example

Divide: $(4x^2 + 2x) \div 2x$

Draw the top of a rectangle with a side length of $2x$.

$x \quad x$

Now, create the rest of a rectangle that represents the dividend, $4x^2 + 2x$. In order to get sections that total $4x^2$, draw two rows of width x.

Since the last term of the dividend is $2x$, rows of length 1 are needed to make x sections. Each row of length 1 makes sections that total $2x$. So only one row of length 1 is needed.

	x	x
x	x^2	x^2
x	x^2	x^2
1	x	x

The polynomial that corresponds with the width of the rectangle is $2x + 1$.

Therefore, $(4x^2 + 2x) \div 2x = 2x + 1$.

Practice

Directions: For Numbers 1 through 8, multiply or divide the polynomials.

1. $(3x - 6)(2x + 9)$

2. $(4x^3 - 6x^2 + 12x) \div 2x$

3. $(3y^3 + 11y^2 - 25y - 25) \div (y + 5)$

4. $(3x^2 - 5)(x^3 + 6x^2 - 8x + 3)$

5. $4x^2y^3(6x^2 - 5xy + y^2)$

6. $(3x^3 - 7x^2 + 11x - 3) \div (x^2 - 2x + 3)$

7. $(4x - 3)(5x^2 + 7x)$

8. $(3x^4 - 7x^3 - 9x^2 + 41x - 20) \div (3x^2 + 5x - 4)$

SATP Practice begins on the following page.

1. **Divide:** $\frac{-16x^4y^5z^2}{32x^8yz^2}$

A $-2x^4y^4$

B $-\frac{y^4z}{2x^4}$

C $-\frac{y^5z}{2x^2}$

D $-\frac{y^4}{2x^4}$

---

2. **Subtract:** $(3x^2 + 4x + 6) - (-x^2 + 5x + 7)$

F $4x^2 - x - 1$

G $-4x^2 + x + 1$

H $2x^2 + 9x + 13$

J $-4x - 9x - 13$

---

3. **Simplify:** $(-4m^4n^2)^3$

A $-12m^{12}n^6$

B $-12m^7n^5$

C $-64m^{12}n^6$

D $-64m^7n^5$

---

4. **Simplify:** $\sqrt{36x^4y^6z^2}$

F $18x^2y^4$

G $18x^2y^3z$

H $6x^2y^4$

J $6x^2y^3z$

---

5. **Multiply:** $(4x^2y)(-3x^4y^5)$

A $-12x^6y^5$

B $-12x^6y^6$

C $-12x^8y^5$

D $-12x^8y^6$

---

6. Multiply: $(x - 11)(x - 11)$

F $x^2 - 121$

G $x^2 + 22x - 121$

H $x^2 - 22x + 121$

J $x^2 + 121$

---

7. Multiply: $(3x + 6)(x^2 - 5x + 9)$

A $3x^3 + 6x^2 + x + 54$

B $3x^3 - 9x^2 + 15x + 3$

C $3x^3 + 6x^2 + 9x + 15$

D $3x^3 - 9x^2 - 3x + 54$

---

8. Simplify: $4(2x^2 + 3x - 5) + 2x(3x - 6)$

F $14x^2 - 20$

G $8x^2 + 18x - 8$

H $8x^2 + 18x - 32$

J $14x^2 + 12x - 32$

---

9. Divide: $(6x^2 - x - 35) \div (3x + 7)$

A $3x + 5$

B $3x - 5$

C $2x + 5$

D $2x - 5$

---

10. Simplify: c^{-6}

F $-6c$

G $-c^6$

H $\frac{1}{c^6}$

J $-\frac{c}{6}$

Lesson 7: Factoring Polynomials

In this lesson, you will review the processes for factoring binomials and trinomials.

Greatest Common Factor (GCF)

A **factor** of a real number is any real number that divides the real number evenly (with no remainder).

Write the factors of 8, 12, and 37.

factors of 8: 1, 2, 4, and 8

factors of 12: 1, 2, 3, 4, 6, and 12

factors of 37: 1 and 37

The **greatest common factor (GCF)** of two or more real numbers is the greatest real number that divides each of the real numbers evenly.

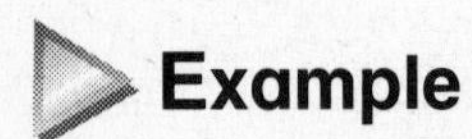

Find the GCF of 18 and 24.

You need to find the greatest number that divides both 18 and 24 evenly. List the factors of each and choose the greatest number that appears in both lists.

factors of 18: 1, 2, 3, **6**, 9, and 18

factors of 24: 1, 2, 3, 4, **6**, 8, 12, and 24

The GCF of 18 and 24 is 6.

Another way to find the GCF is to guess and check. Find any common factor of the numbers and divide. Then, look at the quotients and see if you can find another common factor. If you do, divide again and check for more common factors until there are none. Finally, multiply all the common factors that you have divided by.

$18 \div \mathbf{3} = 6 \rightarrow 6 \div \mathbf{2} = 3$

$24 \div \mathbf{3} = 8 \rightarrow 8 \div \mathbf{2} = 4$

GCF: $3 \cdot 2 = 6$

The GCF of 18 and 24 is 6.

You can also find the GCF of two or more monomials. To do so, find the GCF of the coefficients of each monomial. Then, find the variable(s) that are common to each monomial. If there are any variables that are common, use the smallest exponent that the variable is raised to in the monomials. Remember that 1 is a common factor of every real number and every monomial.

Example

Find the GCF of $15x^2y$ and $20xy$.

The GCF of 15 and 20 is 5.

Notice that both x and y are common to both monomials. The smallest exponent on x is 1 and the smallest exponent on y is 1. So, xy is common to both monomials.

The GCF of $15x^2y$ and $20xy$ is $5xy$.

Practice

Directions: For Numbers 1 through 8, write the GCF for each.

1. 21, 49

   GCF ______________

2. 4, 32

   GCF ______________

3. 6, 9, 18

   GCF ______________

4. 3, 5, 8

   GCF ______________

5. $6xyz$, $8xyz$

   GCF ______________

6. abd, $3abc$

   GCF ______________

7. $4a^2$, $2a$, 6

   GCF ______________

8. $9x^3$, $12x^2$, $18x$

   GCF ______________

Factoring the GCF From a Polynomial

The first step in any factoring process is to factor the GCF from the terms of the polynomial. Factoring the GCF from a polynomial is the inverse (opposite) of multiplying using the distributive property. To factor the GCF from a polynomial, follow these steps:

Step 1: **Find the GCF of the terms of the polynomial.** Don't worry about the signs of the terms.

Step 2: **Divide each term of the polynomial by the GCF.** Recall division of monomials from Lesson 6.

Step 3: **Write your answer as the product of the GCF and the new terms of the polynomial from Step 2.**

Example

Factor the GCF from $3x^2 + 6x - 9$.

The GCF of $3x^2$, $6x$, and 9 is 3.

Divide $3x^2$, $6x$, and -9 each by 3.

$\frac{3x^2}{3} = x^2$ $\qquad \frac{6x}{3} = 2x$ $\qquad \frac{-9}{3} = -3$

Write your answer as the product of 3 and $x^2 + 2x - 3$.

$$3x^2 + 6x - 9 = 3(x^2 + 2x - 3)$$

Example

Factor the GCF from $20x^2y - 45xy^2$.

The GCF of $20x^2y$ and $45xy^2$ is $5xy$.

Divide both $20x^2y$ and $-45xy^2$ by $5xy$.

$\frac{20x^2y}{5xy} = 4x$ $\qquad \frac{-45xy^2}{5xy} = -9y$

Write your answer as the product of $5xy$ and $4x - 9y$.

$$20x^2y - 45xy^2 = 5xy(4x - 9y)$$

Practice

Directions: For Numbers 1 through 8, factor the GCF from each polynomial.

1. $4x^2 + 28x + 48$

2. $2x^2 - 32$

3. $x^3 - 4x^2 - 21x$

4. $50x^3 - 72xy^2$

5. $24x^2y + 28xy - 20y$

6. $6x^3 + 18x^2 - 108x$

7. $9x^2y - 9xy^2$

8. $14x^3 - 63x^2y - 35xy^2$

Factoring Trinomials in the Form $ax^2 \pm bx \pm c$

Before you begin factoring trinomials in the form $ax^2 \pm bx \pm c$, you must determine if the trinomial is factorable over the rational number system. This simply means that the trinomial will only contain rational numbers in its factors. If a trinomial has irrational numbers in its factors, or if it cannot be factored at all, it is said to be prime over the rational number system.

You can use the discriminant to determine if a trinomial is factorable over the rational number system. The **discriminant** for trinomials in the form $ax^2 \pm bx \pm c$ is $b^2 - 4ac$. For a trinomial in this form to be factorable over the rational number system, the discriminant must equal a perfect square number. Remember that 0 is also a perfect square. If the trinomial is factorable, it will factor into the product of two binomials. The order in which you write the binomials does not matter. Factoring a trinomial is the inverse of the FOIL process.

Factoring Trinomials in the Form $x^2 \pm bx + c$

Since the first term of the trinomial is x^2, the first term of each binomial will be x (because $x \cdot x = x^2$). To factor a trinomial in the form $x^2 \pm bx + c$, follow these steps:

Step 1: **Determine if the trinomial is factorable over the rational number system by determining if $b^2 - 4ac$ is a perfect square number.**
Notice that $a = 1$ when a trinomial is in this form.

Step 2: **Find two numbers whose product is c and whose sum is $|b|$.**

Step 3: **The signs of the binomials will be the same, they will each be the sign of the middle term of the trinomial.** Since the signs of the binomials are the same, it won't matter which of the two numbers goes in which binomial.

Example

Factor: $x^2 + 8x + 12$

$$b^2 - 4ac = 8^2 - 4(1)(12) = 16$$

$4^2 = 16$, so the trinomial is factorable.

Notice that $c = 12$ and $|b| = 8$. Find two numbers whose product is 12 and whose sum is 8. List the factor pairs of 12.

$1 \cdot 12 = 12$ $\quad$ $2 \cdot 6 = 12$ $\quad$ $3 \cdot 4 = 12$

The factor pair of 12 with a sum of 8 is 2 and 6.

Since the sign on the middle term of the trinomial $x^2 + 8x + 12$ is +, the signs of both binomials will be +.

Write the trinomial equal to the product of two binomials whose first terms are x and whose second terms are 2 and 6.

$$x^2 + 8x + 12 = (x + 2)(x + 6) \quad [\text{or } (x + 6)(x + 2)]$$

Check your answer by using the FOIL process.

$$(x + 2)(x + 6) = x^2 + 6x + 2x + 12$$
$$= x^2 + 8x + 12$$

Therefore, $x^2 + 8x + 12$ factors to $(x + 2)(x + 6)$.

Example

Factor: $x^2 - 16x + 15$

$$b^2 - 4ac = (-16)^2 - 4(1)(15) = 196$$

$14^2 = 196$, so the trinomial is factorable.

Notice that $c = 15$ and $|b| = 16$. Find two numbers whose product is 15 and whose sum is 16. List the factor pairs of 15.

$1 \bullet 15 = 15 \qquad 3 \bullet 5 = 15$

The factor pair of 15 with a sum of 16 is 1 and 15.

Since the sign on the middle term of the trinomial $x^2 - 16x + 15$ is −, the signs of the binomials will both be −.

Write the trinomial equal to the product of two binomials whose first terms are x and whose second terms are 1 and 15.

$$x^2 - 16x + 15 = (x - 1)(x - 15)$$

Check your answer by using the FOIL process.

$$(x - 1)(x - 15) = x^2 - 15x - x + 15$$
$$= x^2 - 16x + 15$$

Therefore, $x^2 - 16x + 15$ factors to $(x - 1)(x - 15)$.

Practice

Directions: For Numbers 1 through 8, first determine if the given trinomial is factorable over the rational number system. Then, factor each trinomial that can be factored.

1. $x^2 + 18x + 32$

2. $x^2 - 4x + 4$

3. $x^2 - 7x + 6$

4. $x^2 + 10x + 20$

5. $x^2 + 10x + 25$

6. $x^2 - 10x + 21$

7. $x^2 + 7x + 27$

8. $x^2 - 29x + 28$

Objectives: 2h, 2j

Factoring Trinomials in the Form $x^2 \pm bx - c$

Since the first term of the trinomial is x^2, the first term of each binomial will be x (because $x \bullet x = x^2$). To factor a trinomial in the form $x^2 \pm bx - c$, follow these steps:

Step 1: **Determine if the trinomial is factorable over the rational number system by determining if $b^2 - 4ac$ is a perfect square number.**
Notice that $a = 1$ when a trinomial is in this form.

Step 2: **Find two numbers whose product is $|c|$ and whose difference is $|b|$.**

Step 3: **The signs of the binomials will be different (one +, one −).**

Step 4: **The larger of the two numbers from Step 2 goes with the sign of the middle term of the trinomial.**

Example

Factor: $x^2 + 7x - 18$

$$b^2 - 4ac = 7^2 - 4(1)(-18) = 121$$

$11^2 = 121$, so the trinomial is factorable.

Notice that $|c| = 18$ and $|b| = 7$. Find two numbers whose product is 18 and whose difference is 7. List the factor pairs of 18.

$1 \bullet 18 = 18 \qquad 2 \bullet 9 = 18 \qquad 3 \bullet 6 = 18$

The factor pair of 18 with a difference of 7 is 2 and 9.

Write the trinomial equal to the product of two binomials whose first terms are x and whose second terms are 2 and 9.

$$x^2 + 7x - 18 = (x \_\_ 2)(x \_\_ 9)$$

Since the sign on the middle term of the trinomial $x^2 + 7x - 18$ is +, the 9 goes in the binomial with the + and the 2 goes with the − because $9 - 2 = 7$.

$$x^2 + 7x - 18 = (x - 2)(x + 9)$$

Check your answer by using the FOIL process.

$$(x - 2)(x + 9) = x^2 + 9x - 2x - 18$$
$$= x^2 + 7x - 18$$

Therefore, $x^2 + 7x - 18$ factors to $(x - 2)(x + 9)$.

Example

Factor: $x^2 - 9x - 10$

$$b^2 - 4ac = (-9)^2 - 4(1)(-10) = 121$$

$11^2 = 121$, so the trinomial is factorable.

Notice that $|c| = 10$ and $|b| = 9$. Find two numbers whose product is 10 and whose difference is 9. List the factor pairs of 10.

$$1 \bullet 10 = 10 \qquad 2 \bullet 5 = 10$$

The factor pair of 10 with a difference of 9 is 1 and 10.

Write the trinomial equal to the product of two binomials whose first terms are x and whose second terms are 1 and 10.

$$x^2 - 9x - 10 = (x \_\_ 1)(x \_\_ 10)$$

Since the sign on the middle term of the trinomial $x^2 - 9x - 10$ is $-$, the 10 goes in the binomial with the $-$ and the 1 goes with the $+$ because $-10 + 1 = -9$.

$$x^2 - 9x - 10 = (x + 1)(x - 10)$$

Check your answer by using the FOIL process.

$$(x + 1)(x - 10) = x^2 - 10x + x - 10$$
$$= x^2 - 9x - 10$$

Therefore, $x^2 - 9x - 10$ factors to $(x + 1)(x - 10)$.

Objectives: 2h, 2j **DOK 1, 2**

Practice

Directions: For Numbers 1 through 8, first determine if the given trinomial is factorable over the rational number system. Then, factor each trinomial that can be factored.

1. $x^2 + 12x - 13$

2. $x^2 - 2x - 35$

3. $x^2 - 2x - 3$

4. $x^2 + 2x - 6$

5. $x^2 + 2x - 63$

6. $x^2 - 44x - 45$

7. $x^2 + 15x - 34$

8. $x^2 - 47x - 48$

Factoring Trinomials in the Form $ax^2 \pm bx \pm c$

To factor a trinomial in the form $ax^2 \pm bx \pm c$, follow these steps:

Step 1: **Determine if the trinomial is factorable over the rational number system by determining if $b^2 - 4ac$ is a perfect square number.** Notice that $a \neq 1$ when a trinomial is in this form.

Step 2: **Find the product of a and $|c|$.**

Step 3: **Find two numbers whose product is the same as the product from Step 2 and whose sum or difference is $|b|$, depending on whether c is positive (sum) or negative (difference).**

Step 4: **Rewrite the middle term of the trinomial as two terms using the factor pair from Step 2 as the coefficients.** If c is positive, the signs on the factor pair will be the same, whichever the sign of the middle term of the trinomial is. If c is negative, the signs on the factor pair will be different with the larger number of the factor pair having the same sign as the sign of the middle term of the trinomial.

Step 5: **Group the first two terms and the last two terms of the new polynomial from Step 3 and factor the GCF from each.** Sometimes the GCF will be 1 or −1.

Step 6: **Write your answer as the product of the common binomial and the binomial formed by the GCFs from Step 4.**

Objectives: 2h, 2j

Example

Factor: $8x^2 - 19x + 6$

$b^2 - 4ac = (-19)^2 - 4(8)(6) = 169$

$13^2 = 169$, so the trinomial is factorable.

Find the product of a and $|c|$. ($a = 8$ and $c = 6$)

$8 \cdot 6 = 48$

Find two numbers whose product is 48 and whose sum (since c is positive) is 19. List the factor pairs of 48.

$1 \cdot 48 = 48$ $\quad 2 \cdot 24 = 48$ $\quad 3 \cdot 16 = 48$

$4 \cdot 12 = 48$ $\quad 6 \cdot 8 = 48$

The factor pair of 48 with a sum of 19 is 3 and 16.

Rewrite the middle term ($-19x$) of the trinomial using the 3 and 16 as coefficients. Since c is positive and the sign on the middle term is $-$, the signs on $3x$ and $16x$ will be the same: they'll both be $-$.

$8x^2 - 19x + 6 = 8x^2 - 3x - 16x + 6$

Group the first two terms ($8x^2$ and $-3x$) and the last two terms ($-16x$ and 6) of the new polynomial.

$(8x^2 - 3x) + (-16x + 6)$

Factor the GCF from each grouping. The GCF of $8x^2$ and $-3x$ is x, and the GCF of $-16x$ and 6 is -2. (Use -2 to keep the first term of the group positive after you factor the GCF.)

$8x^2 - 3x = x(8x - 3)$ $\qquad -16x + 6 = -2(8x - 3)$

Notice that the binomial within the ( ) in both cases is the same. That is the common binomial. The other binomial in your answer will be formed from the GCFs of the two groupings ($x - 2$).

$8x^2 - 19x + 6 = (8x - 3)(x - 2)$ $\quad$ [or $(x - 2)(8x - 3)$]

Check your answer by using the FOIL process.

$(8x - 3)(x - 2) = 8x^2 - 16x - 3x + 6$

$= 8x^2 - 19x + 6$

Therefore, $8x^2 - 19x + 6$ factors to $(8x - 3)(x - 2)$.

Example

Factor: $5x^2 - 23x - 10$

$b^2 - 4ac = (-23)^2 - 4(5)(-10) = 729$

$27^2 = 729$, so the trinomial is factorable.

Find the product of a and $|c|$. ($a = 5$ and $c = -10$)

$5 \bullet 10 = 50$

Find two numbers whose product is 50 and whose difference (since c is negative) is 23. List the factor pairs of 50.

$1 \bullet 50 = 50 \qquad 2 \bullet 25 = 50 \qquad 5 \bullet 10 = 50$

The factor pair of 50 with a difference of 23 is 2 and 25.

Rewrite the middle term ($-23x$) of the trinomial using 2 and 25 as coefficients. Since c is negative and the sign on the middle term is $-$, the signs on $2x$ and $25x$ will be different and $25x$ will have the same sign as the middle term of the trinomial ($-$).

$5x^2 - 23x - 10 = 5x^2 - 25x + 2x - 10$

Group the first two terms ($5x^2$ and $-25x$) and the last two terms ($2x$ and -10) of the new polynomial.

$(5x^2 - 25x) + (2x - 10)$

Factor the GCF from each grouping. The GCF of $5x^2$ and $-25x$ is $5x$, and the GCF of $2x$ and -10 is 2.

$5x^2 - 25x = 5x(x - 5) \qquad 2x - 10 = 2(x - 5)$

Notice that the binomial within the ( ) in both cases is the same. That is the common binomial. The other binomial in your answer will be formed from the GCFs of the two groupings ($5x + 2$).

$5x^2 - 23x - 10 = (x - 5)(5x + 2)$

Check your answer by using the FOIL process.

$(x - 5)(5x + 2) = 5x^2 + 2x - 25x - 10$

$= 5x^2 - 23x - 10$

Therefore, $5x^2 - 23x - 10$ factors to $(x - 5)(5x + 2)$.

Objectives: 2h, 2j **DOK 1, 2**

Practice

Directions: For Numbers 1 through 8, first determine if the given trinomial is factorable over the rational number system. Then, factor each trinomial that can be factored.

1. $6x^2 - 5x - 4$

2. $2x^2 + 21x + 27$

3. $10x^2 - 39x + 14$

4. $4x^2 + 3x - 27$

5. $3x^2 + 17x + 10$

6. $12x^2 - 9x - 15$

7. $5x^2 + 4x - 9$

8. $9x^2 - 6x + 1$

Factoring Binomials in the Form $m^2 - n^2$

Binomials in the form $m^2 - n^2$ are called the "difference of two squares." Notice that both terms of the binomial are perfect squares and they are separated by −. Recall from Lesson 6 that perfect square monomials have perfect square coefficients and even exponents on every variable. Binomials in this form will factor into the product of two binomials. The order in which you write the binomials does not matter. To factor a binomial in the form $m^2 - n^2$, follow this formula:

$$m^2 - n^2 = (m + n)(m - n)$$

Example

Factor: $x^2 - 25$

Be sure both terms of the binomial are perfect squares.

x^2: coefficient is 1, a perfect square; exponent is even

25: a perfect square

Find the square root of each term.

$\sqrt{x^2} = x \qquad \sqrt{25} = 5$

Substitute the square roots of the terms in the formula.

$x^2 - 25 = (x + 5)(x - 5) \quad [\text{or } (x - 5)(x + 5)]$

Check your answer by using the FOIL process.

$$(x + 5)(x - 5) = x^2 - 5x + 5x - 25$$
$$= x^2 - 25$$

Therefore, $x^2 - 25$ factors to $(x + 5)(x - 5)$.

TIP: Binomials in the form $m^2 + n^2$ are prime over the rational number system.

Example

Factor: $9x^2 - 49y^4$

Be sure both terms of the binomial are perfect squares.

$9x^2$: coefficient is 9, a perfect square; exponent is even

$49y^4$: coefficient is 49, a perfect square; exponent is even

Find the square roots of each term.

$\sqrt{9x^2} = 3x$ $\sqrt{49y^4} = 7y^2$

Substitute the square roots of the terms in the formula.

$9x^2 - 49y^4 = (3x + 7y^2)(3x - 7y^2)$

Check your answer by using the FOIL process.

$$(3x + 7y^2)(3x - 7y^2) = 9x^2 - 21xy^2 + 21xy^2 - 49y^4$$
$$= 9x^2 - 49y^4$$

Therefore, $9x^2 - 49y^4$ factors to $(3x + 7y^2)(3x - 7y^2)$.

Practice

Directions: For Numbers 1 through 8, first determine if the given binomial is factorable over the rational number system. Then, factor each binomial that can be factored.

1. $x^2 - 4$

2. $16x^2 - 1$

3. $25x^2 - 81$

4. $4x^2 + 121$

5. $x^2 - 100y^6$

6. $36x^2 - 169$

7. $16x^2 - 8y^2$

8. $144x^2 - y^8$

People in Math

Edwin Hubble
(1889–1953)

For centuries, astronomers were completely occupied with studying the objects in our own galaxy, the Milky Way. And who could blame them? After all, there's plenty to learn about our galactic neighbors. But in the 1920s, Edwin Hubble made an astonishing discovery: There are many galaxies beyond our own.

As a child growing up in Missouri and Illinois, Hubble was better known for his interest in sports than in scholarship. But by the time he left for college, he'd become serious about learning. Hubble attended the University of Chicago and Oxford University. He then served as a high-ranking officer in World War I.

In 1919, Hubble began working at the Mount Wilson Observatory in California. This gave him access to the 200-inch Hale Telescope. It was the finest telescope in the world at the time. Hubble used his astronomy and math skills to measure the distance to a blurry patch of stars called the Andromeda Nebula. And he discovered something amazing. That blurry patch was actually an entire galaxy! It is similar in appearance to our galaxy, but it is about 2.5 million light-years away.

Hubble applied his findings to other distant galaxies. He had found that astronomers could measure distances based on the brightness of stars and planets. This discovery unlocked the universe to scientists and scholars.

Hubble died before he could accept his Nobel Prize. He received another great honor when the *Hubble Space Telescope* was named after him. Since 1990, Edwin Hubble's namesake telescope has orbited Earth, relaying amazing images from faraway galaxies.

Objectives: 2h, 2j

Completely Factoring Polynomials

You have reviewed the individual processes for factoring polynomials of different types in this lesson. When you factor, always see if you can factor a greatest common factor from the polynomial first. Then, try to factor any remaining binomial or trinomial according to its type. Check all polynomials in your answer to see if they can be factored again. There may be some polynomials that can be factored a number of times. Be sure all factors are included in your final answer. The order in which you write the binomials does not matter.

Example

Factor: $2x^4 - 4x^3 - 70x^2$

Check for a GCF. The GCF of $2x^4$, $4x^3$, and $70x^2$ is $2x^2$. Factor $2x^2$ from the trinomial.

$$2x^4 - 4x^3 - 70x^2 = 2x^2(x^2 - 2x - 35)$$

Don't assume you're done at this point. Check to see if you can factor the resulting trinomial $(x^2 - 2x - 35)$.

$$b^2 - 4ac = (-2)^2 - 4(1)(-35) = 144$$

$12^2 = 144$, so the trinomial is factorable.

Recall factoring a trinomial in the form $x^2 - bx - c$.

$$x^2 - 2x - 35 = (x + 5)(x - 7) \quad [\text{or } (x - 7)(x + 5)]$$

Check to see if you can factor $x + 5$ and/or $x - 7$ again. Neither can be factored again (they do not fit the "difference of two squares" form).

Be sure to go back and find all the different factors that have been factored from the original polynomial for your final answer.

$$2x^4 - 4x^3 - 70x^2 = 2x^2(x^2 - 2x - 35)$$
$$= 2x^2(x + 5)(x - 7) \quad [\text{or } 2x^2(x - 7)(x + 5)]$$

Check your answer by multiplying using the distributive property and/or the FOIL process.

$$2x^2(x + 5)(x - 7) = (2x^3 + 10x^2)(x - 7)$$
$$= 2x^4 - 14x^3 + 10x^3 - 70x^2$$
$$= 2x^4 - 4x^3 - 70x^2$$

Therefore, $2x^4 - 4x^3 - 70x^2$ factors to $2x^2(x + 5)(x - 7)$.

Example

Factor: $16x^4 - 81$

Check for a GCF. The GCF of $16x^4$ and 81 is 1. Factoring by 1 doesn't change the binomial. Continue with the other factoring processes.

Check and see if you can factor the binomial. The binomial is in the form of the "difference of two squares." Factor accordingly.

$$16x^4 - 81 = (4x^2 + 9)(4x^2 - 9)$$

Check to see if you can factor $4x^2 + 9$ and/or $4x^2 - 9$ again. You cannot factor $4x^2 + 9$ again, but you can factor $4x^2 - 9$ again: it also is in the "difference of two squares" form.

$$4x^2 - 9 = (2x + 3)(2x - 3)$$

Check to see if you can factor $2x + 3$ and/or $2x - 3$ again. Neither can be factored again.

Find all the different factors that have been factored from the original polynomial for your final answer.

$$\begin{aligned} 16x^4 - 81 &= (4x^2 + 9)(4x^2 - 9) \\ &= (4x^2 + 9)(2x + 3)(2x - 3) \end{aligned}$$

Check your answer by multiplying using the distributive property and/or the FOIL process.

$$\begin{aligned} (4x^2 + 9)(2x + 3)(2x - 3) &= (8x^3 + 12x^2 + 18x + 27)(2x - 3) \\ &= 16x^4 - 24x^3 + 24x^3 - 36x^2 + 36x^2 - 54x + 54x - 81 \\ &= 16x^4 - 81 \end{aligned}$$

Therefore, $16x^4 - 81$ factors to $(4x^2 + 9)(2x + 3)(2x - 3)$.

Objectives: 2h, 2j **DOK 1**

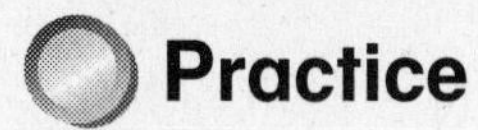

Practice

Directions: For Numbers 1 through 8, completely factor each polynomial.

1. $24x^2 + 6x - 30$

2. $81x^4 - 625$

3. $4x^4 - 12x^3 - 112x^2$

4. $8x^3 + 14x^2 + 3x$

5. $128x^3 - 98x$

6. $15x^2y - 93xy + 18y$

7. $12x^2 - 13x - 14$

8. $48x^5y - 3xy^3$

SATP Practice begins on the following page.

1. Which of the following justifies that $x^2 + 8x - 20$ is NOT prime over the rational number system?

A $x^2 + 8x - 20$ factored is $(x + 4)(x - 5)$.

B $x^2 + 8x - 20$ factored is $(x + 5)(x - 4)$.

C $x^2 + 8x - 20$ factored is $(x + 10)(x - 2)$.

D $x^2 + 8x - 20$ factored is $(x + 2)(x - 10)$.

---

2. Factor: $16x^2 - 25$

F $(4x - 5)(4x - 5)$

G $(4x + 5)(4x - 5)$

H $(2x - 5)(8x - 5)$

J $(2x + 5)(8x - 5)$

---

3. Factor: $49x^2 - 484$

A $(7x - 22)(7x - 22)$

B $(7x + 22)(7x - 22)$

C $(22x - 7)(22x - 7)$

D $(22x + 7)(22x - 7)$

---

4. Factor: $18x^3 - 51x^2 + 15x$

F $3x(6x^2 - 18x + 5)$

G $3x(6x^3 - 17x^2 + 5x)$

H $3x(2x - 1)(3x - 5)$

J $3x(3x - 1)(2x - 5)$

---

5. **Factor: $5x^4 - 65x^3 + 200x^2$**

A $5x^2(x - 5)(x - 8)$

B $5x^2(x + 4)(x - 10)$

C $5x^2(x^2 - 12x + 40)$

D $5x^2(5x^2 - 13x + 50)$

---

6. **What is the GCF of $480a^2b^5c^3$ and $960a^3bc^2$?**

F $120a^3b^5c^3$

G $240a^2bc^2$

H $480a^2bc^2$

J $560abc$

---

7. **Which of the following justifies that $x^2 + 3x + 1$ is prime over the rational number system?**

A The discriminant of $x^2 + 3x + 1$ is a non-perfect square.

B The discriminant of $x^2 + 3x + 1$ is a perfect square.

C The discriminant of $x^2 + 3x + 1$ is a rational number.

D The discriminant of $x^2 + 3x + 1$ is a prime number.

---

8. **Factor: $4x^3y^3 - 2x^2y^3 + 8xy^3$**

F $2xy^2(2x^2y^2 - xy + 4y^2)$

G $2xy^3(2x + 2)(2x - 2)$

H $2xy^3(x - 2)(x + 1)$

J $2xy^3(2x^2 - x + 4)$

Lesson 8: Absolute Value and Quadratic Equations

In this lesson, you will graph and analyze absolute value equations. You will also review how to graph and solve quadratic equations using different methods.

Absolute Value Equations

An **absolute value equation** has the form $y = a|x - h| + k$, where $a \neq 0$. The graph of an absolute value equation of this form is V-shaped, either opening upward or downward. The point of the "V," the **vertex**, is located at (h, k).

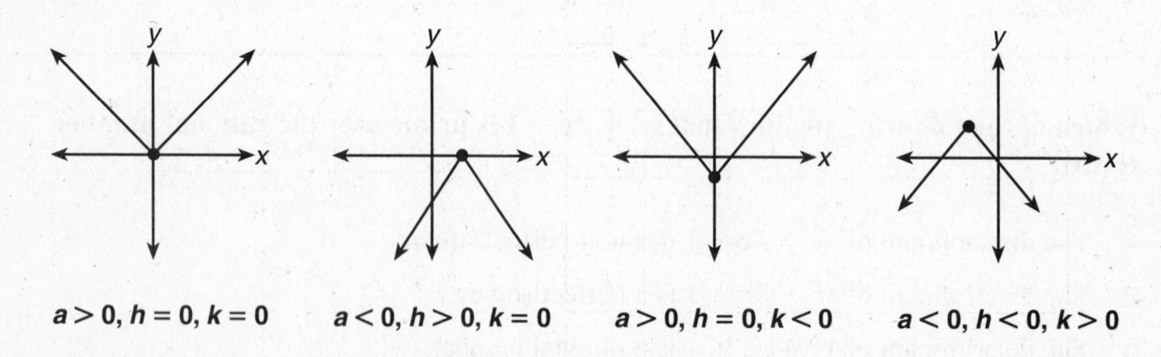

Changing the *h*-value shifts the points of the graph to the right (greater *h*-values) or to the left (lesser *h*-values). Changing the *k*-value shifts the points of the graph up (greater *k*-values) or down (lesser *k*-values). If $a > 0$, the graph opens upward. If $a < 0$, the graph opens downward.

Since the absolute value is defined for every real number, the domain of an absolute value equation of this form is the set of all real numbers. The range depends on the values of a and k. If $a > 0$, the range is the set of real numbers greater than or equal to k. If $a < 0$, the range is the set of real numbers less than or equal to k.

A solution to an absolute value equation is any ordered pair that makes the equation true. An absolute value equation of this form has two zeros. It might have two real-number zeros (the graph intersects the *x*-axis at two distinct points), one real-number zero (the vertex is on the *x*-axis) and one non-real-number zero, or no real-number zeros (the graph never intersects the *x*-axis) and two non-real-number zeros.

Objectives: 2k

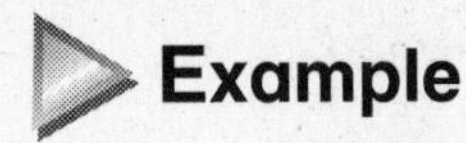

Example

Make a table of values for the absolute value equation $y = 3|x + 1| - 2$. First, find the x-coordinate of the vertex of the graph to determine which x-values to use in the table. Then, graph the equation. What are some characteristics of the equation?

The value of h is -1. Therefore, the x-coordinate of the vertex of the graph is -1. Use x-values in the table on either side of -1.

x	$y = 3\|x + 1\| - 2$	y
-4	$y = 3\|-4 + 1\| - 2$	7
-3	$y = 3\|-3 + 1\| - 2$	4
-2	$y = 3\|-2 + 1\| - 2$	1
-1	$y = 3\|-1 + 1\| - 2$	-2
0	$y = 3\|0 + 1\| - 2$	1
1	$y = 3\|1 + 1\| - 2$	4
2	$y = 3\|2 + 1\| - 2$	7

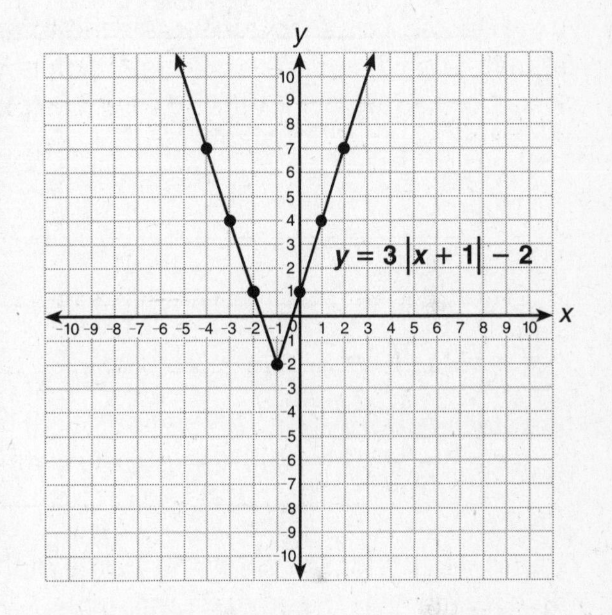

The value of k is -2. The graph of the equation is V-shaped with a vertex of $(-1, -2)$.

The value of a is 3. Since $a > 0$, the graph opens upward.

The domain of the equation is the set of all real numbers. Since $a > 0$, the range is the set of real numbers greater than or equal to -2 ($k = -2$).

Since the graph intersects the x-axis in two places, the equation has two real-number zeros. These are the x-intercepts of the graph.

Practice

Directions: For Numbers 1 and 2, fill in the table for the given equation. Choose *x*-values on both sides of the *x*-coordinate of the vertex of the graph. Then, graph the equation.

1. $y = -|x| - 4$

x	$y = -\|x\| - 4$	y

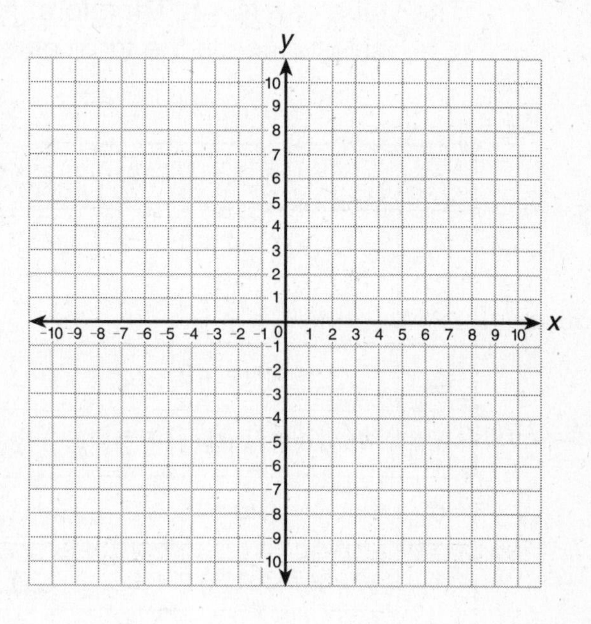

2. $y = 4|x + 1| - 5$

x	$y = 4\|x + 1\| - 5$	y

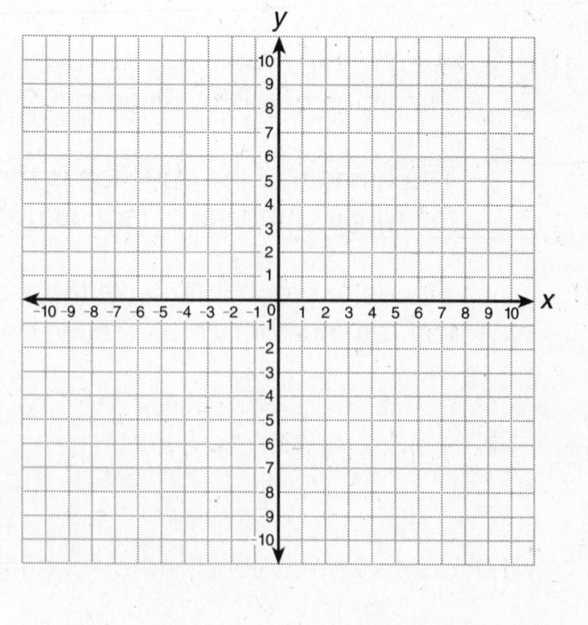

Directions: Use the following absolute value equation to answer Numbers 3 through 7.

$y = -2|x + 3| + 1$

3. Describe the graph. Be sure to include the vertex and which way it opens.

____

____

4. What is the domain? ______________________

5. What is the range? ______________________

6. What are three solutions of the equation? ______________________

7. How many real-number zeros does the equation have? __________

Directions: Use the following absolute value equation to answer Numbers 8 through 12.

$y = |x - 7|$

8. Describe the graph. Be sure to include the vertex and which way it opens.

____

____

9. What is the domain? ______________________

10. What is the range? ______________________

11. What are three solutions of the equation? ______________________

12. How many real-number zeros does the equation have? __________

Graphing Quadratic Equations

A **quadratic equation** has the form $y = ax^2 + bx + c$, where $a \neq 0$. The graph of a quadratic equation is a curve called a **parabola**. The solutions to a quadratic equation are called **roots**. When you find the roots of a quadratic equation that has been set equal to zero, you are finding the **zeros** of the quadratic equation. On a coordinate plane, the zeros occur when the graph of the equation crosses the line $y = 0$, which is the x-axis. A quadratic equation might have two real-number zeros (the graph intersects the x-axis at two distinct points), one real-number zero (the vertex is on the x-axis), or no real-number zeros (the graph never intersects the x-axis).

One side of a parabola is a reflection of the other. Once you have found the "turn-around" point, called the **vertex**, all you need to do is find the "mirror images" of the other points that have been plotted. The line of reflection, called the **axis of symmetry**, is the vertical line that passes through the vertex. The x-coordinate of the vertex is $-\frac{b}{2a}$. Once this value is found, it can be substituted for x in the quadratic equation to find the y-coordinate of the vertex.

Example

Make a table of values for and graph the quadratic equation, $y = -x^2 + 4x + 5$. Then, identify the number of real-number zeros of the equation.

The vertex of the graph of the equation is located at the point (2, 9). Use x-values in the table on either side of 2.

x	$y = -x^2 + 4x + 5$	y
−1	$y = -(-1)^2 + 4(-1) + 5$	0
0	$y = -(0)^2 + 4(0) + 5$	5
1	$y = -(1)^2 + 4(1) + 5$	8
2	$y = -(2)^2 + 4(2) + 5$	9
3	$y = -(3)^2 + 4(3) + 5$	8
4	$y = -(4)^2 + 4(4) + 5$	5
5	$y = -(5)^2 + 4(5) + 5$	0

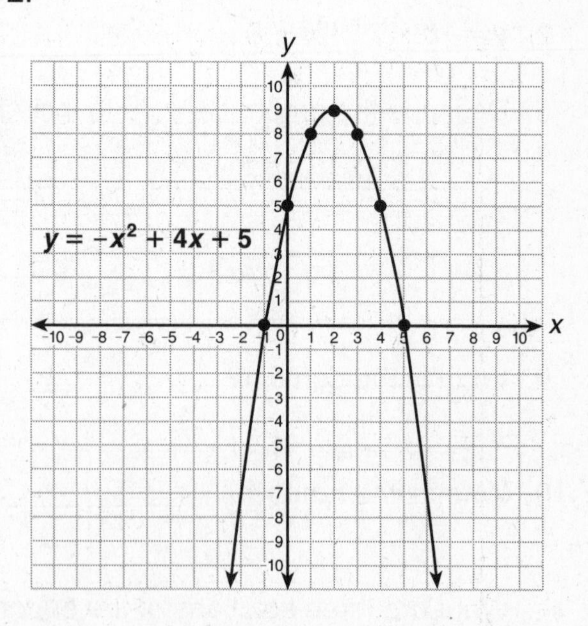

The graph of the equation has two x-intercepts. This means the equation has two real-number zeros. In this example, the zeros are located at $x = -1$ and $x = 5$.

Practice

Directions: For Numbers 1 and 2, fill in the table for the given equation by choosing x-values near the x-coordinate of the vertex. Then, graph the equation and identify the number of real-number zeros of the equation.

1. $y = x^2 - 4x + 5$

x	$y = x^2 - 4x + 5$	y

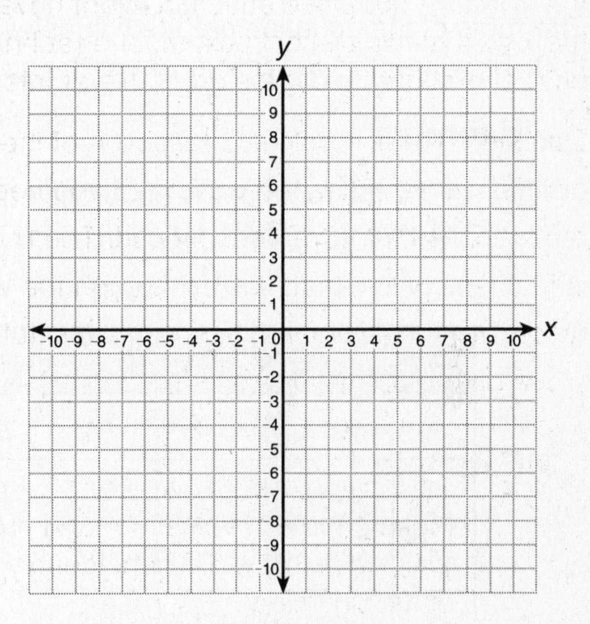

number of real-number zeros ________

2. $y = -2x^2 - 4x + 8$

x	$y = -2x^2 - 4x + 8$	y

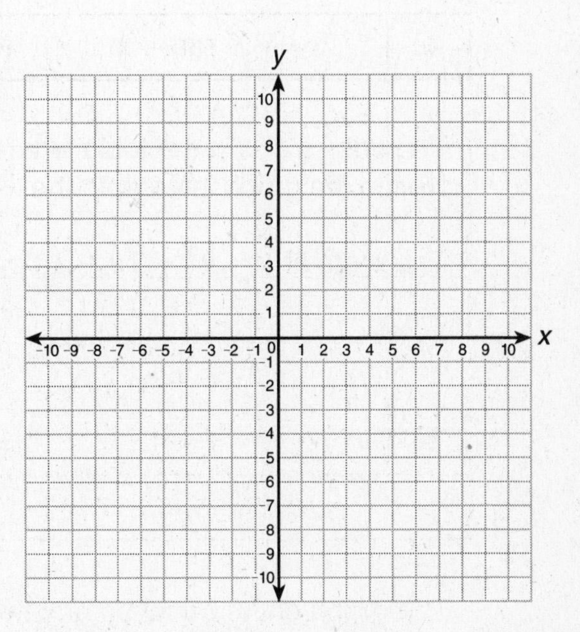

number of real-number zeros ________

Solving Quadratic Equations

There are many ways to solve a quadratic equation. You can solve a quadratic equation by graphing, factoring, completing the square, and using the quadratic formula.

Using Graphs to Solve Quadratic Equations

The roots of the equation are the values of *x* in a table where the *y*-values are equal to 0. They are also the points where the graph of the equation intercepts the *x*-axis.

Example

Find the roots of the quadratic equation $y = x^2 + 7x + 10$.
(Solve $x^2 + 7x + 10 = 0$.)

x	$y = x^2 + 7x + 10$	y
-6	$y = (-6)^2 + 7(-6) + 10$	4
-5	$y = (-5)^2 + 7(-5) + 10$	0
-4	$y = (-4)^2 + 7(-4) + 10$	-2
-3	$y = (-3)^2 + 7(-3) + 10$	-2
-2	$y = (-2)^2 + 7(-2) + 10$	0
-1	$y = (-1)^2 + 7(-1) + 10$	4
0	$y = 0^2 + 7(0) + 10$	10

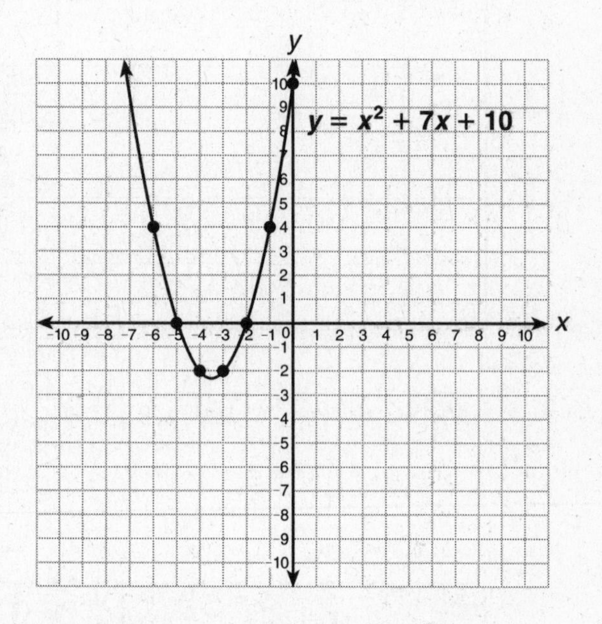

The values of *x* in the table where the *y*-values are equal to 0 are −5 and −2. Notice the graph intercepts the *x*-axis at −5 and −2.

The roots of $y = x^2 + 7x + 10$ are −5 and −2.

Practice

Directions: For Numbers 1 and 2, fill in the table and draw the graph of the given quadratic equation. Use the table and graph to find the roots of the equation.

1. $y = x^2 - 4x + 3$

x	$y = x^2 - 4x + 3$	y
−1		
0		
1		
2		
3		
4		
5		

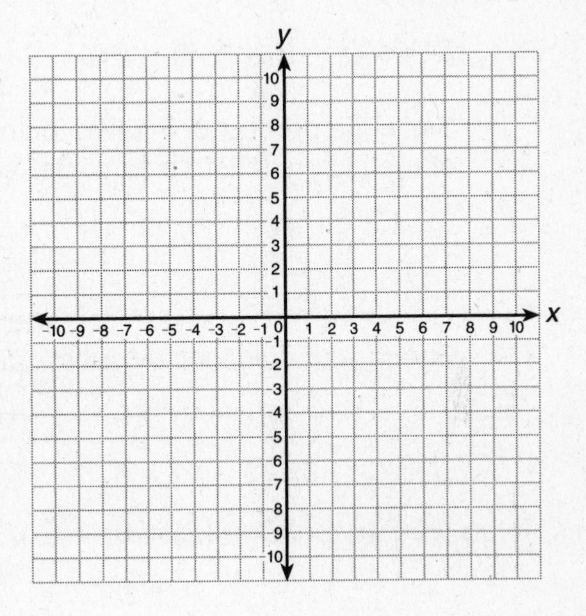

2. $y = x^2 - 2x - 8$

x	$y = x^2 - 2x - 8$	y
−3		
−2		
−1		
0		
1		
2		
3		
4		
5		

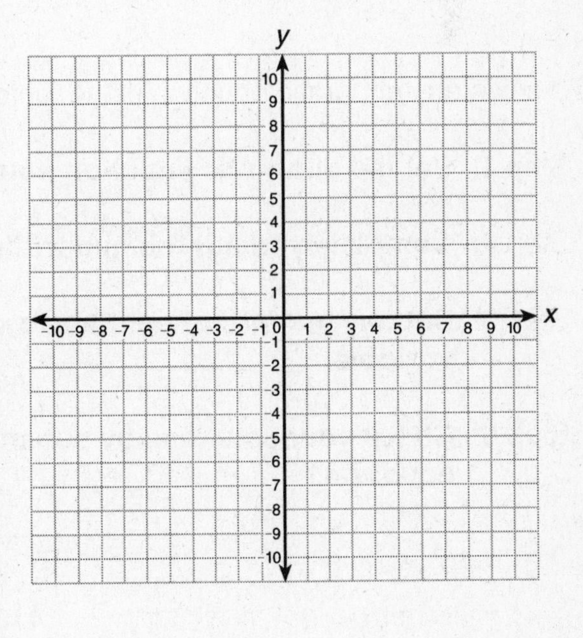

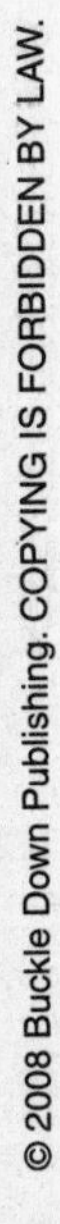

Factoring to Solve Quadratic Equations

The zeros of a quadratic equation can be found using factoring. It is important to remember that any time you multiply two or more factors and your product is 0, at least one of the factors must be zero. This is called the **zero-product property**.

Example

Solve: $(x + 3)(x - 9) = 0$

Since the product of the two factors is zero, by the zero-product property, one of the factors must be zero. Set each factor equal to zero and solve for x.

$x + 3 = 0$ or $x - 9 = 0$

$x = -3$ $\quad$ $x = 9$

Check your solutions by substituting each of them into the original equation.

$$(x + 3)(x - 9) = 0 \quad \text{or} \quad (x + 3)(x - 9) = 0$$

$$(\mathbf{-3} + 3)(\mathbf{-3} - 9) = 0 \qquad (\mathbf{9} + 3)(\mathbf{9} - 9) = 0$$

$$(0)(-12) = 0 \qquad (12)(0) = 0$$

$$0 = 0 \qquad 0 = 0$$

Since the substitution makes both equations true, $x = -3$ or $x = 9$.

To solve any quadratic equation using factoring, follow these steps:

Step 1: **Set the quadratic equation equal to zero.**

Step 2: **Completely factor the quadratic equation.**

Step 3: **Set any factor that contains a variable equal to zero; then, solve for the variable.**

Step 4: **Check your solutions by substituting each of them into the original equation.**

Objectives: 2i, 2k

Example

What are the zeros of the following quadratic equation?

$$y = x^2 + 4x - 45$$

Set the quadratic equation equal to zero.

$$x^2 + 4x - 45 = 0$$

Completely factor the quadratic equation.

$$x^2 + 4x - 45 = 0$$

$$(x - 5)(x + 9) = 0$$

According to the zero-product property, at least one of $x - 5$ or $x + 9$ must be zero. Set each factor equal to zero and solve for the variable.

$$x - 5 = 0 \quad \text{or} \quad x + 9 = 0$$

$$x = 5 \qquad\qquad x = -9$$

Check your solutions by substituting each of them into the original equation.

$x^2 + 4x - 45 = 0$	or	$x^2 + 4x - 45 = 0$
$\mathbf{5}^2 + 4(\mathbf{5}) - 45 = 0$		$(\mathbf{-9})^2 + 4(\mathbf{-9}) - 45 = 0$
$25 + 20 - 45 = 0$		$81 - 36 - 45 = 0$
$0 = 0$		$0 = 0$

Since the substitution makes both equations true, the zeros of $y = x^2 + 4x - 45$ are 5 and -9.

TIP: Some quadratic equations are written without a y. If you are asked to find the zeros of a quadratic equation without a y, you must rewrite the equation so it is equal to zero before you begin finding the zeros. In the example above, the equation $y = x^2 + 4x - 45$ could have been given as $x^2 - 45 = -4x$. In this case, you would add $4x$ to each side of the equation and then begin finding the zeros.

Sometimes when you factor, the resulting binomials will be the same. Therefore, when you find the zeros, they will be the same. This zero is sometimes called a **double zero**. This occurs when the vertex of the parabola is on the *x*-axis.

Example

What are the zeros of the following quadratic equation?

$$y = 4x^2 + 20x + 25$$

Set the quadratic equation equal to zero.

$$4x^2 + 20x + 25 = 0$$

Completely factor the quadratic equation.

$$4x^2 + 20x + 25 = 0$$

$$(2x + 5)(2x + 5) = 0$$

Set one factor equal to zero and solve for *x*.

$$2x + 5 = 0$$

$$2x = -5$$

$$x = -\frac{5}{2}$$

Check your double zero.

$$4x^2 + 20x + 25 = 0$$

$$4\left(-\frac{5}{2}\right)^2 + 20\left(-\frac{5}{2}\right) + 25 = 0$$

$$4\left(\frac{25}{4}\right) + 20\left(-\frac{5}{2}\right) + 25 = 0$$

$$25 - 50 + 25 = 0$$

$$0 = 0$$

Since the substitution makes the equation true, the double zero of $y = 4x^2 + 20x + 25$ is $-\frac{5}{2}$.

Practice

Directions: For Numbers 1 through 4, find the zeros of each quadratic equation using factoring. Be sure to check your zeros.

1. $y = x^2 + x - 12$

2. $y = x^2 - 2x - 15$

3. $y = 9x^2 - 24x + 16$

4. $-14x = 2x^2 + 20$

Completing the Square to Solve Quadratic Equations

Sometimes it is not easy to factor a quadratic equation. In such cases, you can find the zeros of the equation by performing a process called completing the square.

To solve any quadratic equation by completing the square, follow these steps:

Step 1: **Set the quadratic equation equal to zero.**

Step 2: **Move the constant term, *c*, to the side of the equation opposite the variable terms.**

Step 3: **Divide both sides of the equation by the value of *a*.**

Step 4: **Divide the value of *b* by 2, square the result, and add it to both sides of the equation.**

Step 5: **Write the side of the equation with the variables as a binomial squared, and simplify the side of the equation with the constants.**

Step 6: **Take the square root of each side of the equation. Remember the positive and negative roots of the constant. Then, simplify as necessary.**

Step 7: **Solve for the variable. Remember that there are two solutions, unless the zero is a double zero.**

Step 8: **Check your solutions by substituting each of them into the original equation.**

Example

What are the zeros of the following quadratic equation?

$$y = 4x^2 - 5x - 20$$

Set the quadratic equation equal to zero.

$$4x^2 - 5x - 20 = 0$$

Move the constant term to the side of the equation opposite the variable terms.

$$4x^2 - 5x = 20$$

Divide both sides of the equation by the value of *a*.

$$x^2 - \frac{5}{4}x = 5$$

Divide the value of *b* by 2, square the result, and add it to both sides of the equation.

$$-\frac{5}{4} \div 2 = -\frac{5}{8}$$

$$\left(-\frac{5}{8}\right)^2 = \frac{25}{64}$$

$$x^2 - \frac{5}{4}x + \frac{25}{64} = 5 + \frac{25}{64}$$

Write the side of the equation with the variables as a binomial squared, and simplify the side of the equation with the constants. The binomial is written as $\left(x + \frac{b}{2}\right)$. In this example, $\frac{b}{2}$ is $-\frac{5}{8}$.

$$\left[x + \left(-\frac{5}{8}\right)\right]^2 = \frac{345}{64}$$

Take the square root of each side of the equation. Remember the positive and negative roots of the constant. Then, simplify as necessary.

$$x + \left(-\frac{5}{8}\right) = \pm\sqrt{\frac{345}{64}}$$

$$= \pm\frac{\sqrt{345}}{8}$$

Solve for the variable. Remember that there are two solutions.

$$x = \frac{5}{8} \pm \frac{\sqrt{345}}{8}$$

$$x = \frac{5 + \sqrt{345}}{8} \text{ or } x = \frac{5 - \sqrt{345}}{8}$$

Remember to check your solutions by substituting each of them into the original equation.

The zeros of $y = 4x^2 - 5x - 20$ are $\frac{5 + \sqrt{345}}{8}$ and $\frac{5 - \sqrt{345}}{8}$.

TIP: When the solutions to a quadratic equation contain irrational numbers like the example above, you can find decimal approximations of the solutions. In real-world situations, the decimal approximations may be more helpful or meaningful.

Practice

Directions: For Numbers 1 through 4, find the zeros of each quadratic equation by completing the square. Be sure to check your zeros.

1. $y = x^2 + x - 11$

2. $y = 2x^2 - 2x - 13$

3. $y = 4x^2 - 21x + 15$

4. $y = 2x^2 + 13x + 7$

Objectives: 2i, 2k

Using the Quadratic Formula to Solve Quadratic Equations

To find the zeros of any quadratic equation using the quadratic formula, find the values for *a*, *b*, and *c* from the equation. Then, substitute these values into the quadratic formula and simplify. The following table shows several quadratic equations and the *a*, *b*, and *c* values for each equation. Remember to put the equation in standard form before finding the values for *a*, *b*, and *c*.

Equation	Standard Form	*a, b, c* Values
$4x^2 + 3x - 2 = 0$	$4x^2 + 3x - 2 = 0$	$a = 4, b = 3, c = -2$
$-x^2 + 4 = 3x$	$x^2 + 3x - 4 = 0$	$a = 1, b = 3, c = -4$
$\frac{1}{2}x^2 = 8$	$\frac{1}{2}x^2 - 8 = 0$	$a = \frac{1}{2}, b = 0, c = -8$
$-5x + 3 = 6x^2$	$6x^2 + 5x - 3 = 0$	$a = 6, b = 5, c = -3$

To solve any quadratic equation using the quadratic formula, follow these steps:

Step 1: **Set the quadratic equation equal to zero.**

Step 2: **Find the values of *a*, *b*, and *c*.**

Step 3: **Substitute the values of *a*, *b*, and *c* into the quadratic formula.**

Step 4: **Solve the quadratic formula, following the order of operations.**

Step 5: **Check your solutions by substituting each of them into the original equation.**

Quadratic Formula
If $ax^2 + bx + c = 0, a \neq 0$, then $x = \frac{-b \pm \sqrt{b^2 - 4ac}}{2a}$.

Example

What are the zeros of the following quadratic equation?

$y = x^2 + 2x - 3$

Set the quadratic equation equal to zero.

$x^2 + 2x - 3 = 0$

Find the values of *a*, *b*, and *c*.

$a = 1, b = 2, c = -3$

Substitute the values into the quadratic formula and solve.

$$x = \frac{-b \pm \sqrt{b^2 - 4ac}}{2a}$$

$$x = \frac{-2 \pm \sqrt{2^2 - 4(1)(-3)}}{2(1)}$$

$$x = \frac{-2 \pm \sqrt{16}}{2}$$

$$x = \frac{-2 \pm 4}{2}$$

$x = \frac{-2 + 4}{2}$ or $x = \frac{-2 - 4}{2}$

$x = \frac{2}{2}$ or $x = \frac{-6}{2}$

$x = 1$ or $x = -3$

Check your zeros.

$x^2 + 2x - 3 = 0$	$x^2 + 2x - 3 = 0$
$\mathbf{1}^2 + 2(\mathbf{1}) - 3 = 0$	$(\mathbf{-3})^2 + 2(\mathbf{-3}) - 3 = 0$
$1 + 2 - 3 = 0$	$9 - 6 - 3 = 0$
$0 = 0$	$0 = 0$

Since the substitution makes both equations true, the zeros of $y = x^2 + 2x - 3$ are 1 and -3.

TIP: There will be two real-number zeros if $b^2 - 4ac > 0$, one real-number double zero if $b^2 - 4ac = 0$, and no real-number zeros if $b^2 - 4ac < 0$.

Practice

Directions: For Numbers 1 through 4, find the zeros of each quadratic equation using the quadratic formula. Be sure to check your zeros.

1. $y = x^2 - 10x + 16$

2. $y = 6x^2 - 7x$

3. $y = 3x^2 - 11x - 8$

4. $9x^2 = 36x - 36$

Applications of Quadratic Equations

There are many types of problems that can be solved using quadratic equations.

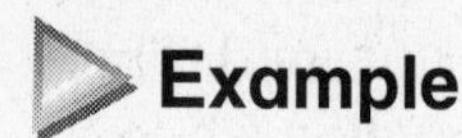

Example

The height of the arch of a tunnel in feet, h, can be modeled by the following quadratic equation where w is the width of the arch in feet.

$$h = -\frac{5}{32}w^2 + \frac{5}{2}w$$

The graph of the equation is shown below.

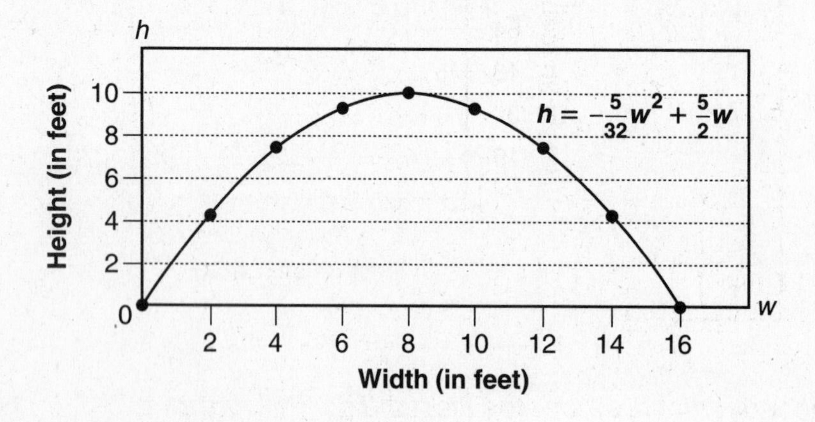

How wide is the arch at its base?

The width of the arch at its base is the distance between the zeros of the equation. Use the graph, factoring, completing the square, or the quadratic formula to find the zeros of the equation.

From the graph, the zeros of the equation are 0 and 16. The distance between the zeros is 16 − 0 or 16 feet.

What is the maximum height of the arch?

The maximum height of the arch is the maximum of the equation. The maximum of the equation is the y-coordinate of the vertex of the equation. From the graph, the vertex is (8, 10).

The maximum height of the arch is 10 feet.

Practice

Directions: Use the following information to answer Numbers 1 through 5.

A ball is kicked straight up into the air with an initial velocity of 64 feet per second. The height of the ball in feet, h, can be modeled by the following quadratic equation where t is the time in seconds after the ball was kicked.

$$h = -16t^2 + 64t$$

1. Fill in the table and draw the graph of the equation.

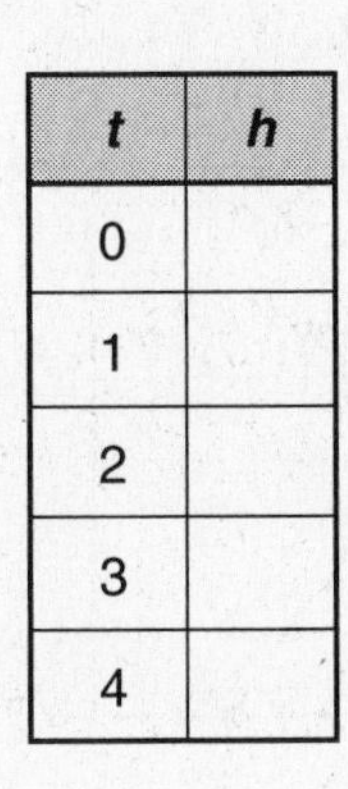

t	h
0	
1	
2	
3	
4	

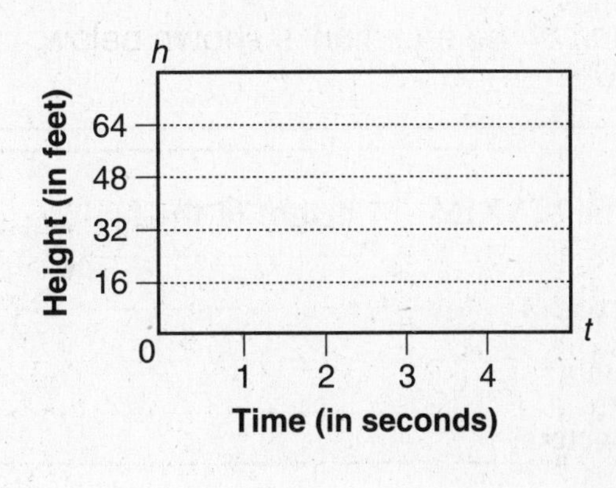

2. How many seconds after the ball was kicked did it hit the ground?

____

3. How many seconds after the ball was kicked did it reach its maximum height?

____

4. What was the maximum height of the ball? __________________

5. What was the exact height of the ball one half of a second after it was kicked?

____

Directions: Use the following information to answer Numbers 1 through 3.

A ball is thrown straight up into the air from an initial height of 49 meters with an initial velocity of 14.7 meters per second. The height of the ball in meters, h, can be modeled by the following quadratic equation, where t is the time in seconds after the ball was thrown.

$$h = -4.9t^2 + 14.7t + 49$$

1. How long after the ball was thrown did it reach its MAXIMUM height?

A 1.5 seconds

B 2.0 seconds

C 2.5 seconds

D 3.0 seconds

---

2. What was the MAXIMUM height of the ball?

F 55.125 meters

G 58.8 meters

H 60.025 meters

J 62.3 meters

---

3. How long after the ball was thrown did it hit the ground?

A 4.25 seconds

B 4.5 seconds

C 4.75 seconds

D 5.0 seconds

---

4. What are the zeros of the following equation?

$$y = 4x^2 - 8x - 5$$

F $-\frac{1}{4}$ and 5

G $-\frac{1}{2}$ and $\frac{5}{2}$

H $-\frac{5}{4}$ and -2

J -1 and $-\frac{5}{4}$

---

5. How many times does the graph of $y = x^2 - 3x + 2$ intersect the x-axis?

A Zero

B One

C Two

D Three

---

6. What are the roots of the equation $x^2 - 3x - 12 = 6$?

F -2 and 9

G -3 and 6

H -6 and 3

J -9 and 2

---

7. What is the GREATEST number of real-number zeros for an absolute value function?

A 0

B 1

C 2

D 3

---

8. Which of the following quadratic equations has no real-number zeros?

F $y = x^2 + 3x + 12$

G $y = x^2 + 3x + 1$

H $y = x^2 + 3x - 12$

J $y = x^2 + 3x - 1$

---

9. What is the range of the following absolute value function?

$$y = -3|x + 4| - 6$$

A The set of real numbers less than or equal to 3

B The set of real numbers less than or equal to -6

C The set of real numbers greater than or equal to 2

D The set of real numbers greater than or equal to -4

---

10. Which graph shows the solution to $y = x^2 - 6$?

F

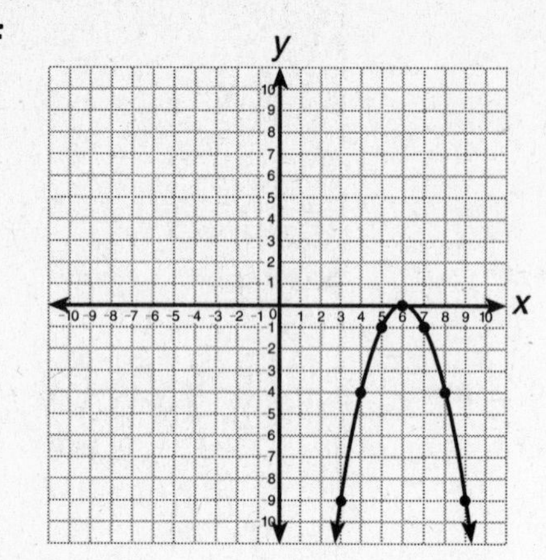

H

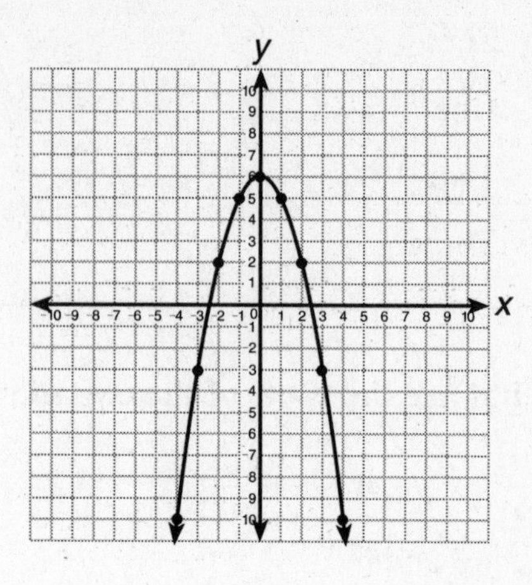

G

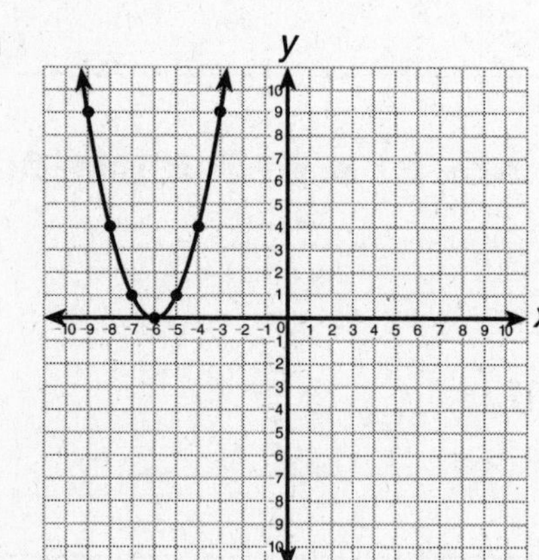

J

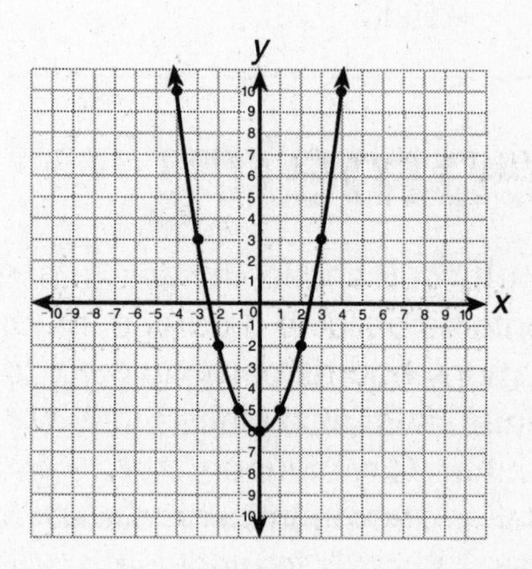

---

11. What are the values of *a*, *b*, and *c* in the following quadratic equation, and what is the solution?

$$4x^2 - 7 = 29$$

A $a = 4, b = -7, c = 29$
solution: $x = 0$ or $x = -3$

B $a = 4, b = -7, c = 29$
solution: $x = 3$ or $x = -3$

C $a = 4, b = 0, c = -36$
solution: $x = 3$ or $x = -3$

D $a = 4, b = 0, c = -36$
solution: $x = 0$ or $x = -3$

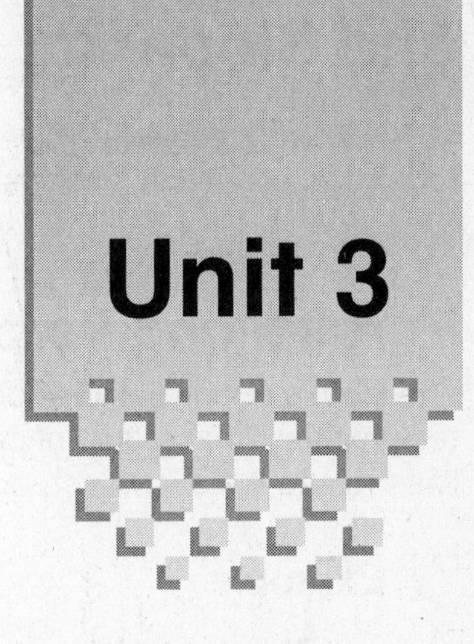

Geometry

Geometry and spatial sense are used every day. If a carpenter is building a garage, he or she needs to place many boards perpendicular to the ground. The carpenter must also place many boards parallel to each other. City planners make roadways that are parallel and perpendicular to each other. Engineers also design roads to meet certain slope requirements so that the rate of change (drop or rise) of the road is not too large for vehicles to travel on.

In this unit, you will review parallel and perpendicular lines. You will also solve problems that involve interpreting slope as a rate of change.

In This Unit

Lesson 9: Parallel and Perpendicular Lines and Slope

In this lesson, you will review the slopes of parallel and perpendicular lines and review real-world situations involving graphs.

Parallel and Perpendicular Lines

The slopes of parallel lines are equal. The slopes of perpendicular lines are opposite reciprocals. The product of opposite reciprocals is -1, so you can multiply the slopes of lines to see if they are perpendicular.

Example

What is the slope of a line that is parallel to $-10x + 5y = 15$?

First, find the slope of $-10x + 5y = 15$ by writing the equation in slope-intercept form ($y = mx + b$, where m is the slope).

$$-10x + 5y = 15$$
$$5y = 10x + 15$$
$$y = 2x + 3$$

The slope of $-10x + 5y = 15$ is 2 ($m = 2$).

Therefore, the slope of a line parallel to $-10x + 5y = 15$ is also 2.

Example

What is the slope of a line that is perpendicular to $77x - 11y = 22$?

First, find the slope of $77x - 11y = 22$.

$$77x - 11y = 22$$
$$-11y = -77x + 22$$
$$y = 7x - 2$$

The slope of $77x - 11y = 22$ is 7. The opposite reciprocal of 7 is $-\frac{1}{7}$.

Therefore, the slope of a line perpendicular to $77x - 11y = 22$ is $-\frac{1}{7}$.

Practice

Directions: For Numbers 1 through 6, find the slope of a line that is parallel to and the slope of a line that is perpendicular to the line with the given linear equation.

1. $-4x - 3y = 9$

   parallel __________

   perpendicular __________

2. $2x + 4y = 3$

   parallel __________

   perpendicular __________

3. $12x - y = 17$

   parallel __________

   perpendicular __________

4. $x = y$

   parallel __________

   perpendicular __________

5. $8x = 3y + 2$

   parallel __________

   perpendicular __________

6. $-2x + y = 5$

   parallel __________

   perpendicular __________

Directions: For Numbers 7 and 8, draw a line that is parallel to, and a line that is perpendicular to, the given line by plotting specific points. Then, give the slope of each line that you drew.

7.

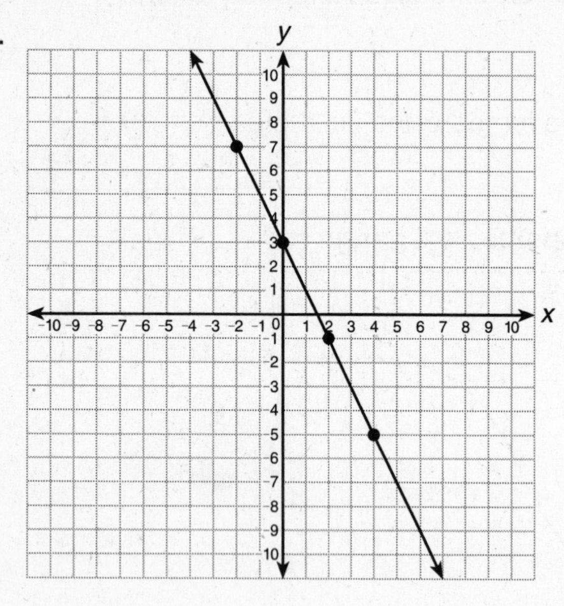

parallel ________

perpendicular ________

8.

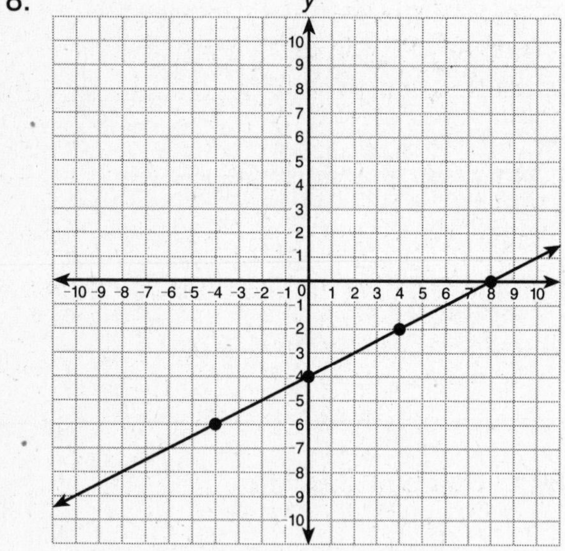

parallel ________

perpendicular ________

9. What is the slope of a line that is parallel to $-18x + 2y = 6$?

   A. -9

   B. 6

   C. 9

   D. 24

10. What is the slope of a line that is perpendicular to $10x - 20y = 0$?

   A. -2

   B. 0

   C. $\frac{1}{2}$

   D. 2

Objectives: 3b

Slope in Real-World Graphs

Graphs can be used to represent many different real-world situations. Being able to gather information about slope, or rate of change, in these graphs is a valuable skill.

Example

The following graph shows how the temperature fluctuated during one 24-hour period.

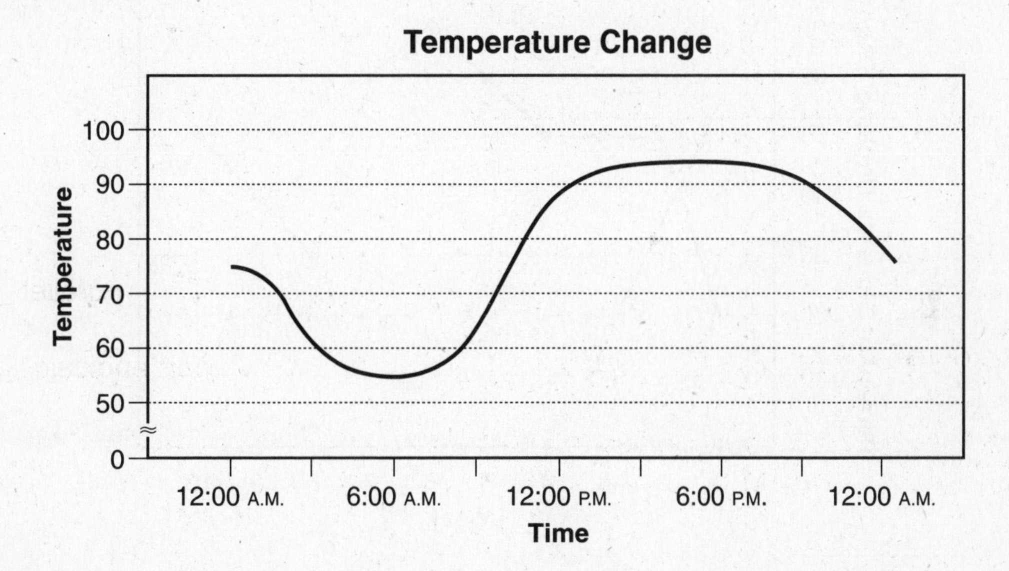

What does the graph show about the temperature from 12:00 A.M. to 6:00 A.M.?

The graph shows that the temperature dropped until around 5:00 A.M., then remained fairly constant until 6:00 A.M.

When did the temperature rise?

The temperature rose from about 7:30 A.M. to about 3:00 P.M.

What does the graph show about the temperature from 6:00 P.M. to 12:00 A.M.?

The graph shows that the temperature dropped gradually from 6:00 P.M. to 9:00 P.M., then dropped more rapidly between 9:00 P.M. and 12:00 A.M.

Example

At the Hattiesburg High School, the algebra class is documenting the change in popularity of fruit smoothies among students over a 10-week period. The results of the experiment are shown in the following graph.

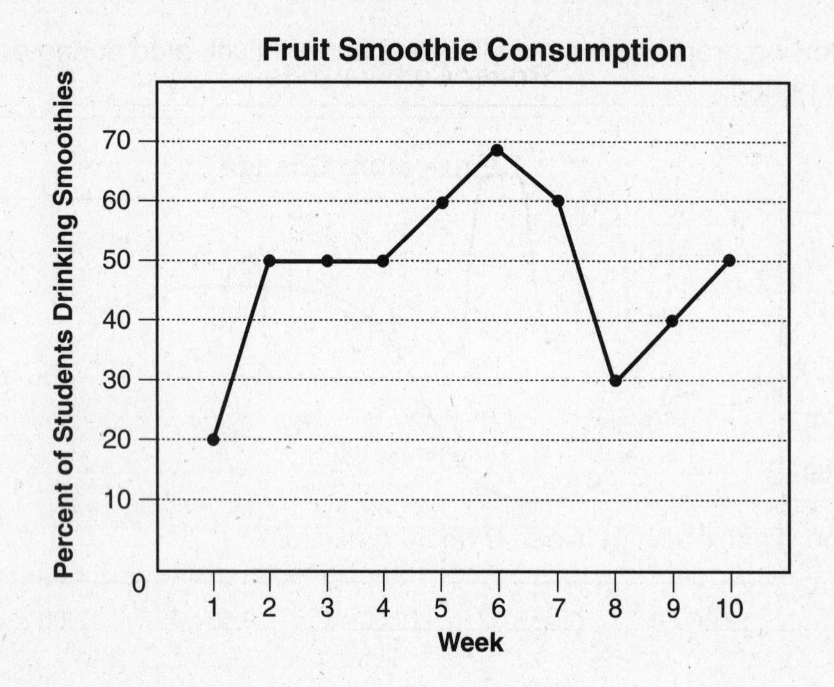

Between which two weeks was the popularity of fruit smoothies decreasing the most?

Examine the graph above to see what behavior the graph shows. The graph shows an increase between weeks 1 and 2, weeks 4 and 6, and weeks 8 and 10. The graph shows no change between weeks 2 and 4. The graph shows a decrease between weeks 6 and 8. The graph is steeper between weeks 7 and 8 than it is between weeks 6 and 7.

The popularity of fruit smoothies was decreasing the most between weeks 7 and 8.

Practice

Directions: Use the following information to answer Numbers 1 through 4.

The following graph shows the height of a person from ground level while riding a roller coaster at the fair.

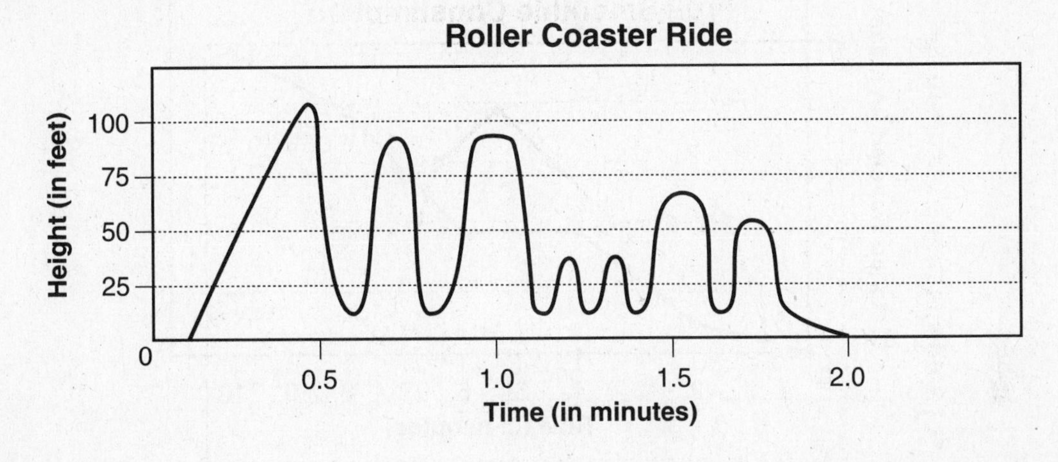

1. What does the graph show between 0 and 0.5 minutes?

____

____

2. What do you think the flat part of the graph around the 1-minute mark represents?

____

____

3. How many times does the height of the rider increase? _______________

4. How many times does the height of the rider decrease? _______________

Directions: Use the following information to answer Numbers 5 through 9.

It took Geoff 10 minutes to drive home from school yesterday. The time and distance increments are shown in the following graph.

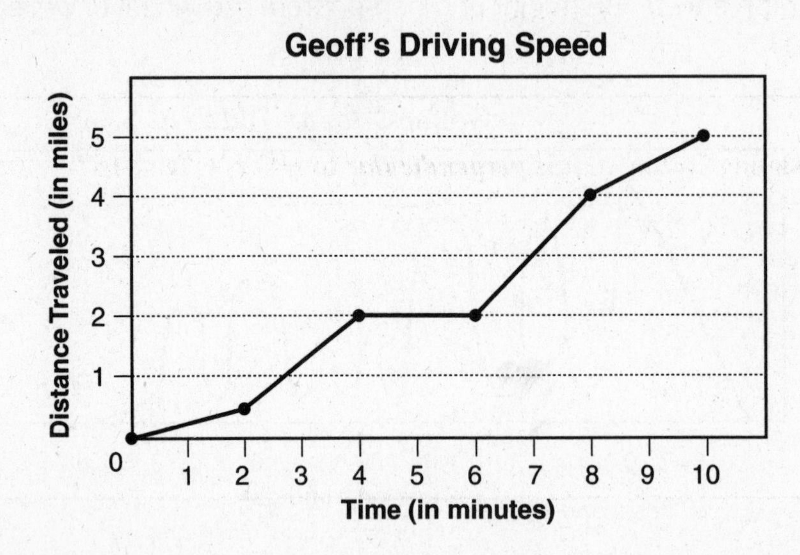

5. How many segments on the graph show the distance Geoff traveled increasing?

____

6. What was Geoff's average rate for the entire trip, in miles per hour?

____

7. In which time interval was Geoff's rate the highest?

____

8. In which time interval was Geoff's rate the lowest?

____

9. What was Geoff's rate between minutes 2 and 4? _______________

SATP Practice begins on the following page.

1. **What is the slope of a line that is *parallel* to $5x - 3y = 6$?**

A $-\frac{5}{3}$

B $-\frac{3}{5}$

C $\frac{3}{5}$

D $\frac{5}{3}$

---

2. **What is the slope of a line that is *perpendicular* to $-42x + 7y = 16$?**

F -6

G $-\frac{1}{6}$

H $\frac{1}{6}$

J 6

---

3. **What is the slope of a line that is *perpendicular* to the following line?**

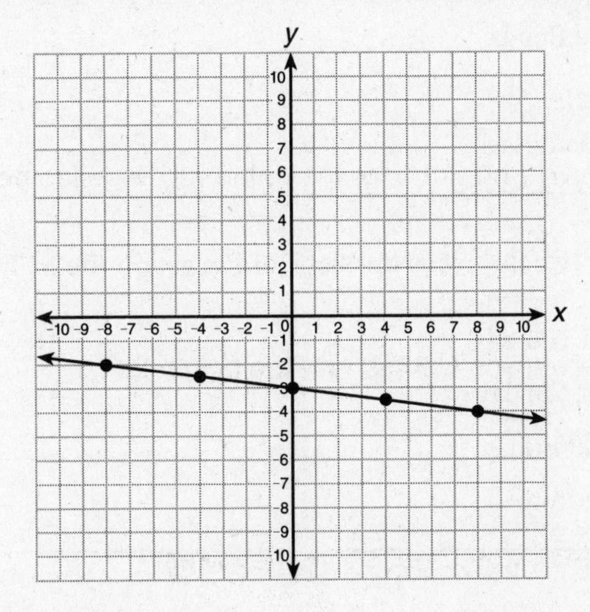

A -8

B $-\frac{1}{8}$

C $\frac{1}{8}$

D 8

Use the following graph to answer Numbers 4 through 6.

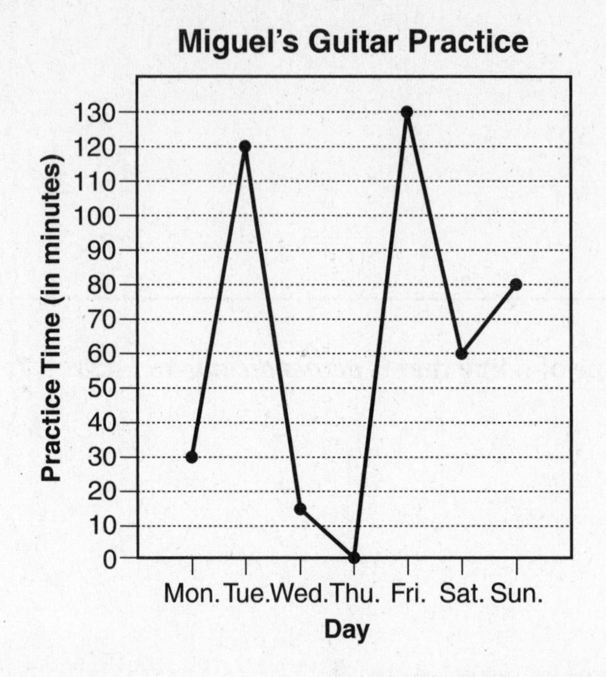

4. Between which two days was the slope of the graph the FLATTEST?

- **F** Tuesday and Wednesday
- **G** Saturday and Sunday
- **H** Wednesday and Thursday
- **J** Friday and Saturday

---

5. Between which two days was the slope of the graph the STEEPEST?

- **A** Monday and Tuesday
- **B** Saturday and Sunday
- **C** Thursday and Friday
- **D** Friday and Saturday

---

6. How many segments on the graph have a slope of zero?

- **F** 0
- **G** 3
- **H** 4
- **J** 6

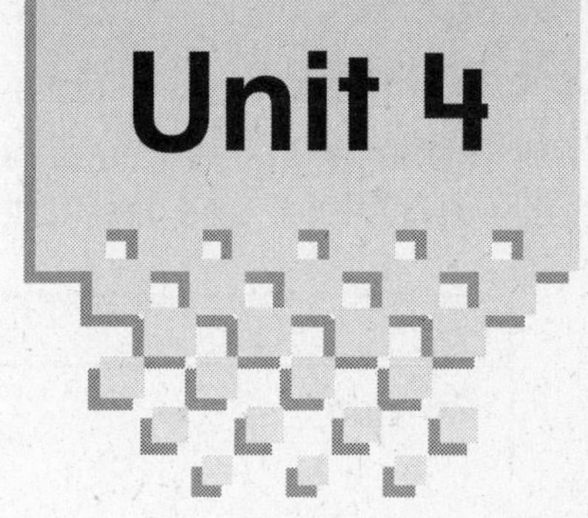

Measurement

Measurement can be as simple as determining how much milk a drinking glass holds, or figuring out how far you live from school. Many jobs rely heavily on measurement. For example, landscapers measure the perimeter of a yard so they can build a fence. They also measure the area of the yard so that they can have the right amount of sod delivered for a new lawn.

In this unit, you will find the perimeter and area of plane figures. You will also solve problems involving distances, rates, and times.

In This Unit

Lesson 10: Solving Measurement Problems

In this lesson you will calculate the perimeter and area of geometric figures. You will also review distance, rate, and time.

Perimeter

Perimeter (*P*) is the distance around a polygon. **Circumference (*C*)** is the distance around a circle. Use the table below to help you answer the practice questions.

Figure	Formula	
Polygon (sides s_1, s_2, s_3, s_4, s_5)	$P = s_1 + s_2 + s_3 + \ldots + s_n$	where s_n = length of side n n = number of sides
Regular Polygon (side l)	$P = l \cdot n$	where l = length of each side n = number of sides
Square (side s)	$P = 4s$	where s = length of each side
Rectangle (w, l)	$P = 2l + 2w$ or $P = 2(l + w)$	where l = length w = width
Circle (r, d)	$C = \pi d$ or $C = 2\pi r$	where d = diameter r = radius $\pi \approx 3.14$

Practice

1. What is the perimeter of this polygon?

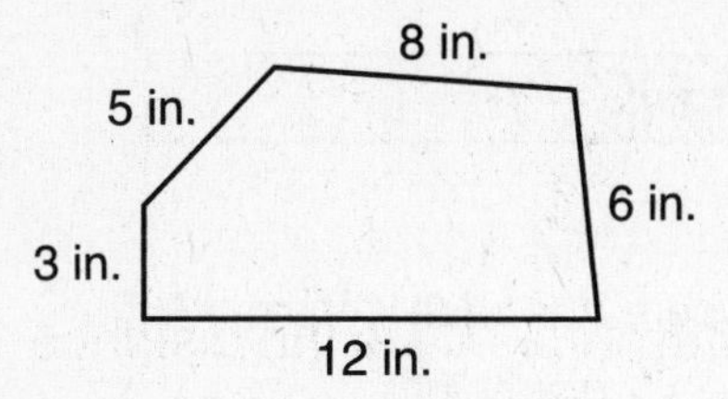

P = ______________

2. What is the perimeter of this parallelogram?

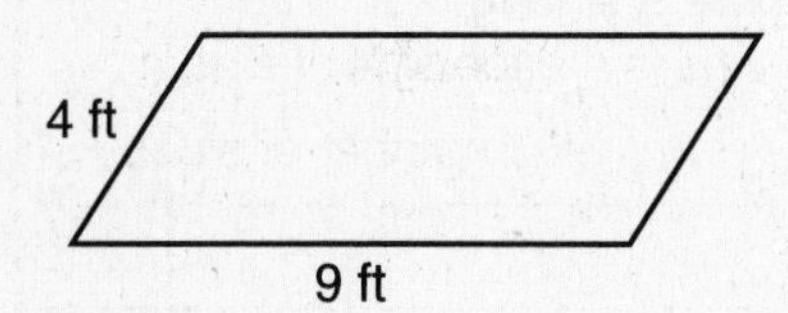

P = ______________

3. The diameter of a golf hole measures 4.25 inches across. What is the circumference of a golf hole? Use 3.14 for π.

C = ______________

4. If the length of each side of a regular hexagon is 38 centimeters, what is the perimeter of the hexagon?

P = ______________

5. The fence around a horse pasture has 12 equal sections. If each section is 12 feet long, what is the perimeter of the horse pasture?

P = ______________

6. If the perimeter of a square is 96 inches, what is the length of each side of the square?

s = ______________

Area

Area (*A*) is the measure of the region inside a closed plane figure. Area is measured in square units. Use the table below to help you answer the practice questions.

Figure	Formula	
triangle 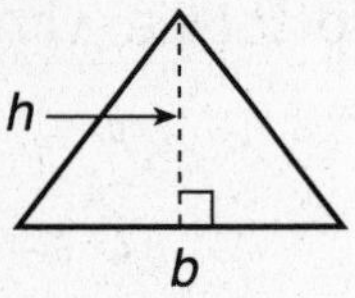	$A = \frac{1}{2}bh$	where b = base length h = height
square 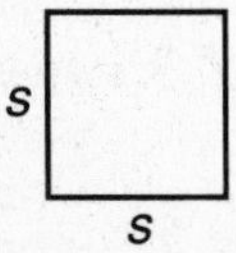	$A = s^2$	where s = length of each side
rectangle 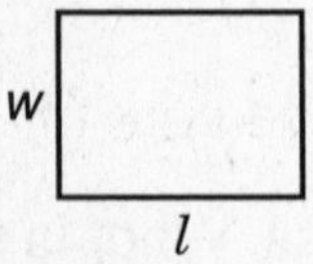	$A = lw$	where l = length w = width
parallelogram 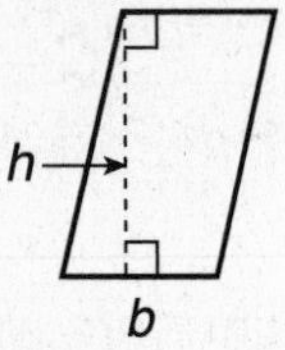	$A = bh$	where b = base length h = height
trapezoid 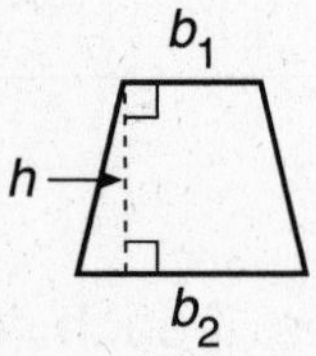	$A = \frac{1}{2}h(b_1 + b_2)$	where b_1 = base 1 length b_2 = base 2 length h = height
circle 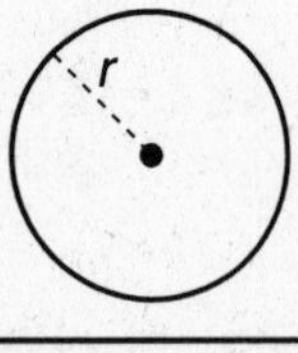	$A = \pi r^2$	where r = radius $\pi \approx 3.14$

TIP: To find the area of a compound figure, add the areas of the simple figures that make up the compound figure.

Practice

1. What is the area of a rectangular poster that measures 2 feet by 1.5 feet?

$A =$ ____________

2. What is the approximate area of a jumbo chocolate chip cookie with a diameter of about 5 inches? Use 3.14 for π.

$A =$ ____________

3. If a parallelogram has an area of 19.22 m^2 and a height of 3.1 meters, what is the length of the base?

$b =$ ____________

4. What is the formula for finding the height of a triangle if you are given its base length and its area?

formula = ____________

5. What is the area of the shaded portion of the following figure in square units?

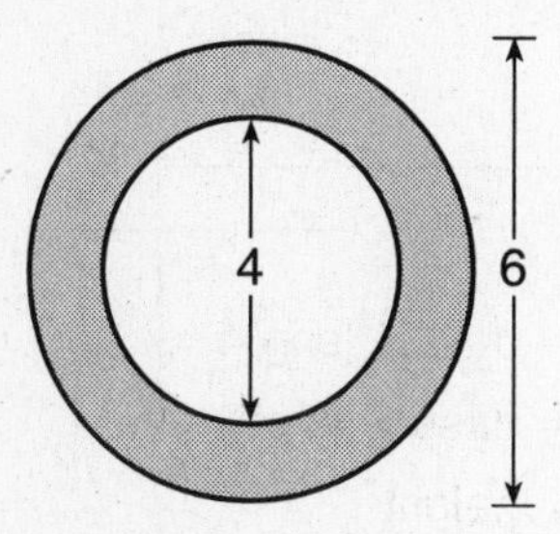

$A =$ ____________

6. What is the area of the shaded cross-section of the following figure? (Round your answer to the nearest tenth.)

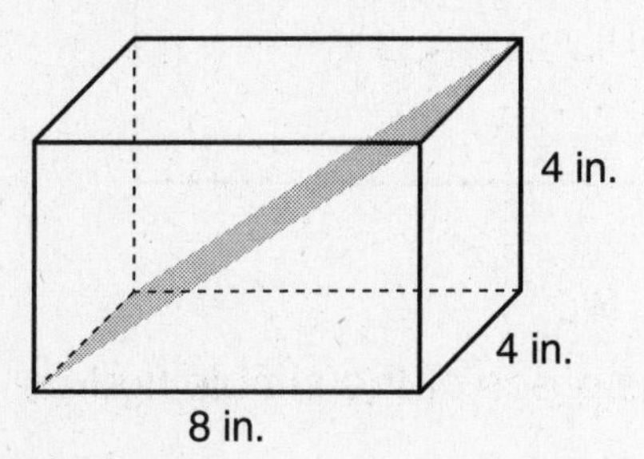

$A =$ ____________

7. What is the area of the following figure?

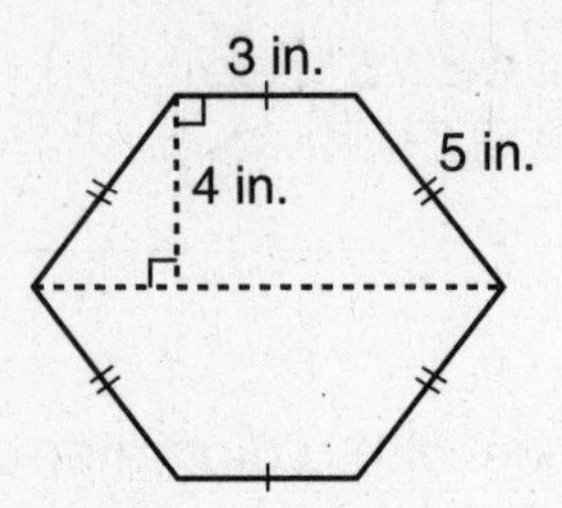

$A =$ ____________

8. What is the area of the following figure?

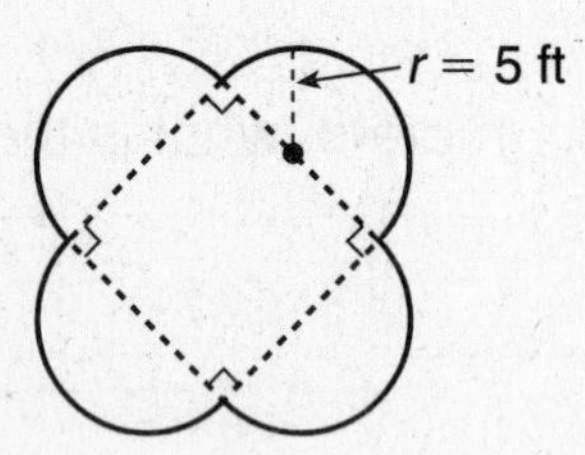

$A =$ ____________

9. If the area of the following figure is 232 cm^2, what is the value of x?

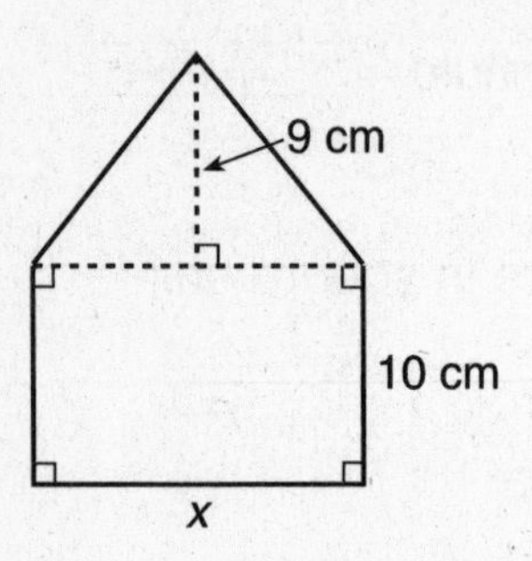

$x =$ ____________

10. What is the area of the following figure?

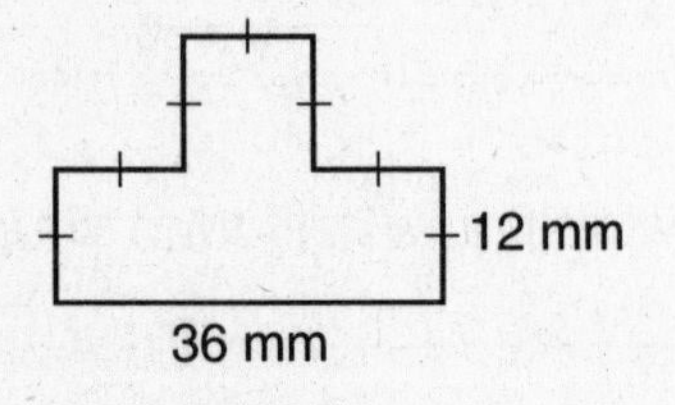

A. 120 mm^2

B. 432 mm^2

C. 480 mm^2

D. 576 mm^2

Objectives: 4c

Applications of Perimeter and Area

You may use computation with polynomials in problem-solving situations. In some cases, it may be helpful to use diagrams to help you see the situation.

Example

Mariah has a flower bed that is 10 feet long and 5 feet wide. She wants to put a fence around the flower bed to keep the deer from eating her flowers. She also wants to leave enough space to walk between the fence and the flower bed. What is the perimeter of the fence if the space between the flower bed and the fence is represented by x?

Make a diagram to represent the situation.

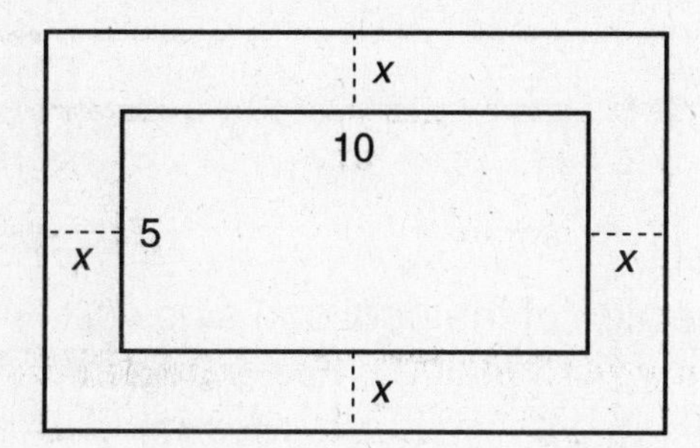

Use the diagram to find the dimensions of the fence.

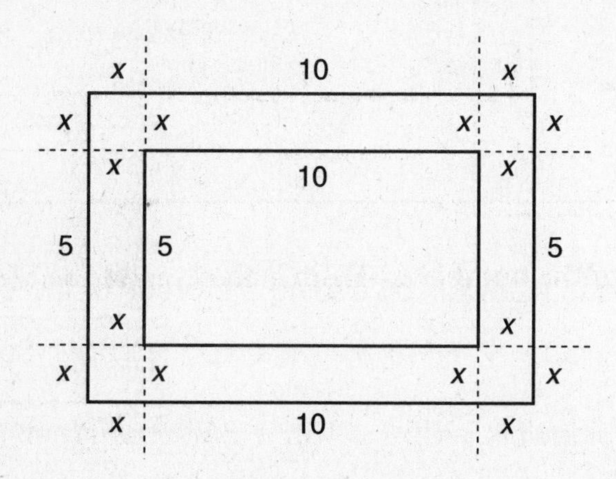

Simplify the expressions representing the lengths of the fence before finding the perimeter of the fence.

$x + 5 + x = 2x + 5$ $\qquad$ $x + 10 + x = 2x + 10$

Find the perimeter of the fence by adding the dimensions.

$$(2x + 5) + (2x + 10) + (2x + 5) + (2x + 10) = 8x + 30$$

The perimeter of the fence is $8x + 30$ feet.

Example

The Mannings want to build a swimming pool in their yard with a 3-foot wide sidewalk around it. They want a pool that is twice as long as it is wide. What area of the yard will the pool and sidewalk take up?

The dimensions of the pool are not given, but we do know how the length relates to the width. Label the length of the pool $2p$ and the width p. Add the dimensions of the sidewalk to the pool.

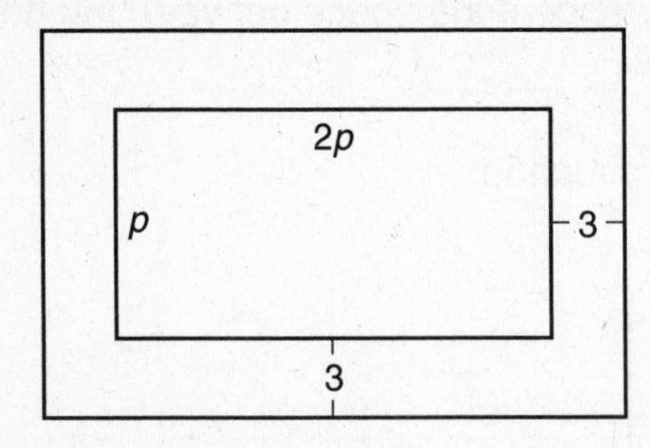

Multiply to find the area of each section of the pool and sidewalk.

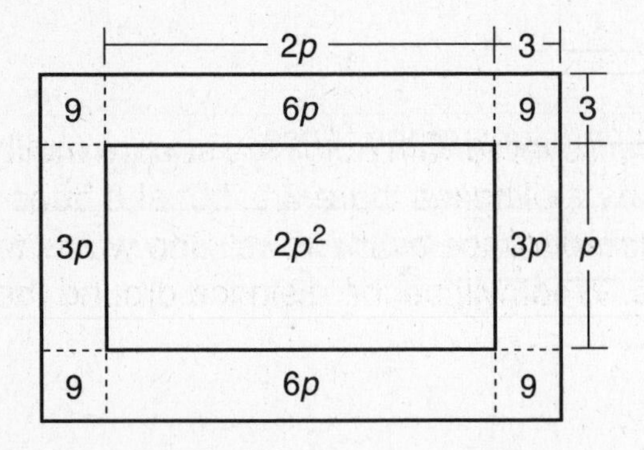

Find the area of the pool and sidewalk by adding the areas of the sections.

$$2p^2 + 6p + 6p + 3p + 3p + 9 + 9 + 9 + 9 = 2p^2 + 18p + 36$$

The area of the pool and sidewalk is $2p^2 + 18p + 36$ square feet.

Practice

1. Tania made a 9 inch by 11 inch cake but is unsure how big of a plate to put it on. She wants to add a border of berries and whipped cream of equal width around the cake but is unsure how wide this will be. What will be the perimeter of the cake, berries, and whipped cream?

   ____

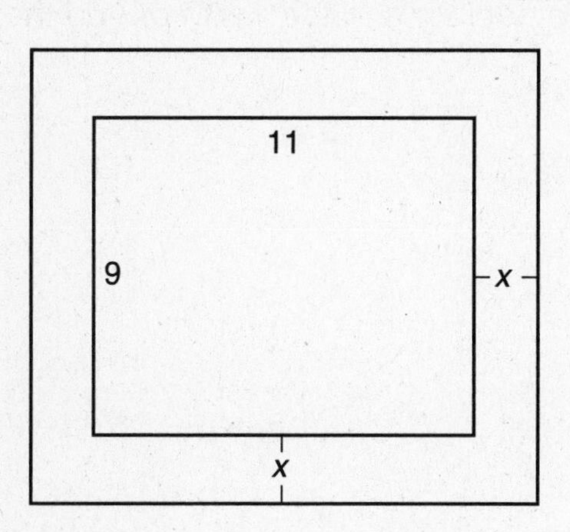

2. The wall of the post office is partially covered with adjoining square mailboxes. The postmaster does not know how many mailboxes there are, but she does know the columns of mailboxes cover twice the distance as the rows. She wants to add 3 rows and 4 columns of mailboxes. What will be the distance around the mailboxes after the addition?

   ____

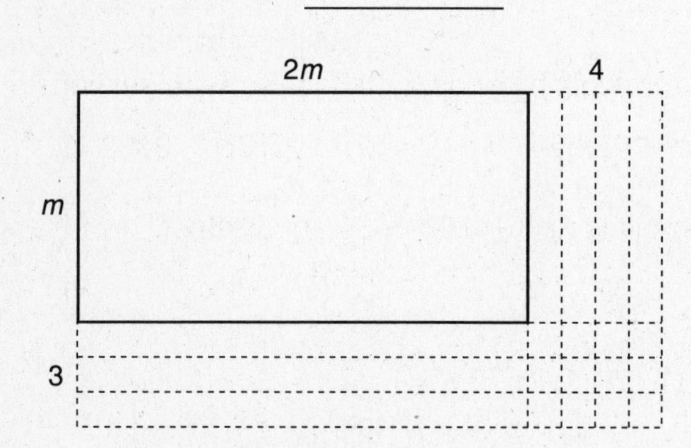

3. Jesse is matting an 8 inch by 10 inch photo. He wants the matte to add the same width, x, to each side, but he does not know how much. What area will the matte and picture take up on the wall?

   ____

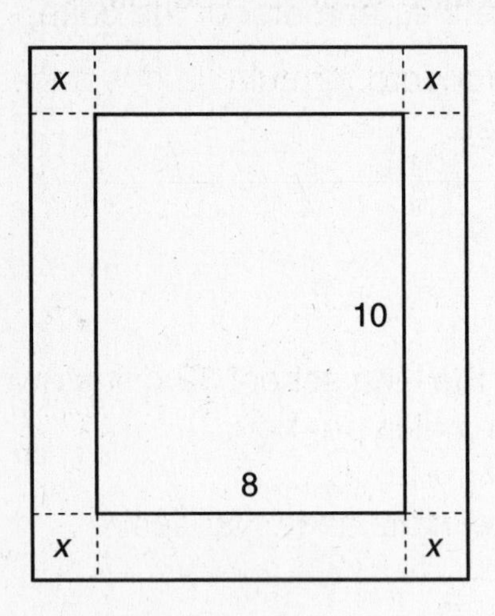

4. The Clarksdale High School is building a new gym. Two basketball courts, each 50 feet by 84 feet, will be included. The school board is still deciding how much space to allow between the courts, so they identified this width as x. What area will the two courts and the space between them cover?

   ____

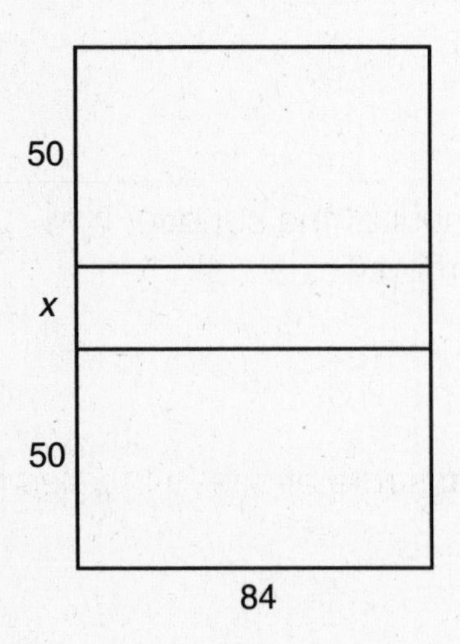

Objectives: 4c **DOK 2**

Distance, Rate, and Time

The formula $d = rt$ shows the relationship between the distance (d) a moving object has traveled, the rate (r) of travel, or the object's speed, and the time (t) it took the object to travel the distance. If two values are known, the third value can be found.

When the value asked for is not the one isolated in the standard formula (in this case, distance), rearrange the formula to isolate the other values.

$\mathbf{d = rt}$ $\mathbf{t = \frac{d}{r}}$ $\mathbf{r = \frac{d}{t}}$

Example

After leaving the art museum, the bus reached the high school 32 miles away in 30 minutes. How fast was the bus traveling in miles per hour?

Define the values and make sure the values are in the units you desire.

$d = 32$ mi $t = 30$ min $= 0.5$ hr $r = ?$

Determine the appropriate formula.

$$d = rt \rightarrow r = \frac{d}{t}$$

Plug in the known values and solve.

$$r = \frac{32 \text{ mi}}{0.5 \text{ hr}} = 64 \text{ mi/hr}$$

The bus was traveling at 64 miles per hour.

Practice

1. If the Mississippi River flows at a rate of 2.5 miles per hour at the surface, how many days would it take a floating object to travel 180 miles?

   ____

2. If a car travels 462 miles in 840 minutes, what is the car's rate of speed in miles per hour?

   ____

3. The radius of a cypress tree increases at the rate of 2.3 inches per year. How many feet has the radius of the tree increased during the last 6 years?

   ____

SATP Practice begins on the following page.

1. **What is the perimeter of the following trapezoid?**

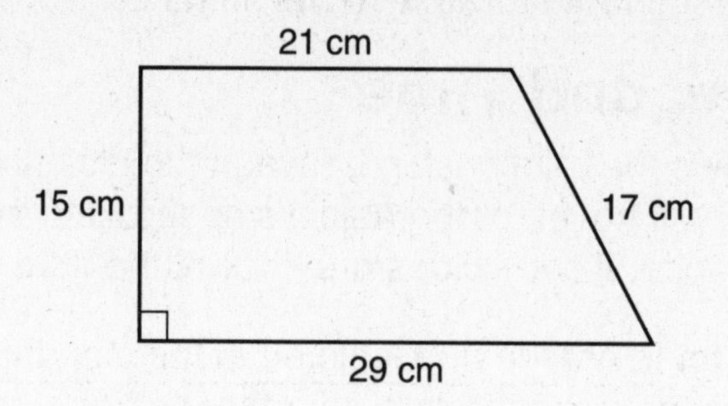

A 41 centimeters

B 57 centimeters

C 66 centimeters

D 82 centimeters

---

2. **The Johnston family has decided to make the new solution to their maze a rectangle. They want to increase the length of the original solution, 1760 feet, by the amount 2*c* and the width, originally 1320 feet, by the amount *c*.**

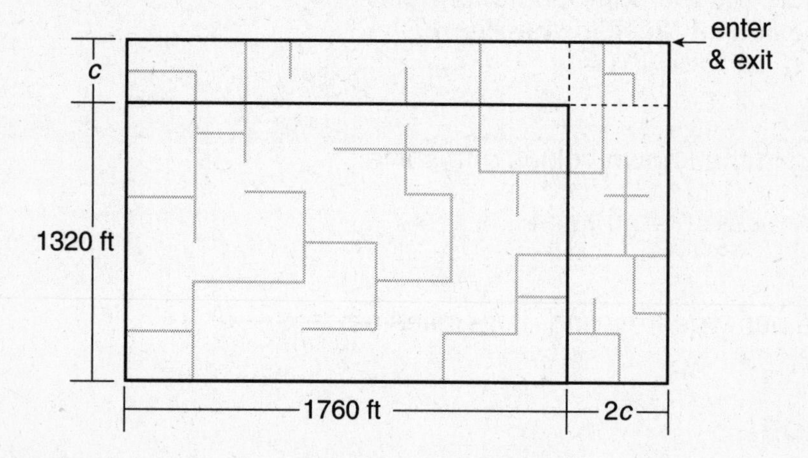

What polynomial represents the perimeter of the solution, in feet?

F $3080 + 3c$

G $6160 + 6c$

H $9240 + 9c$

J $12{,}320 + 12c$

---

3. A crocodile can run 12 feet per second for short periods of time. Assuming a constant rate, how long would it take a crocodile to run 36 *yards*?

A 5 seconds

B 7 seconds

C 9 seconds

D 11 seconds

---

4. Phyllis drove 340 miles from Tupelo, Mississippi, to New Orleans, Louisiana. If it took her 6.25 hours, what was Phyllis's approximate average rate of speed in feet per second?

F 79.8 feet per second

G 81.3 feet per second

H 83.2 feet per second

J 95.0 feet per second

---

5. What is the area of the following figure?

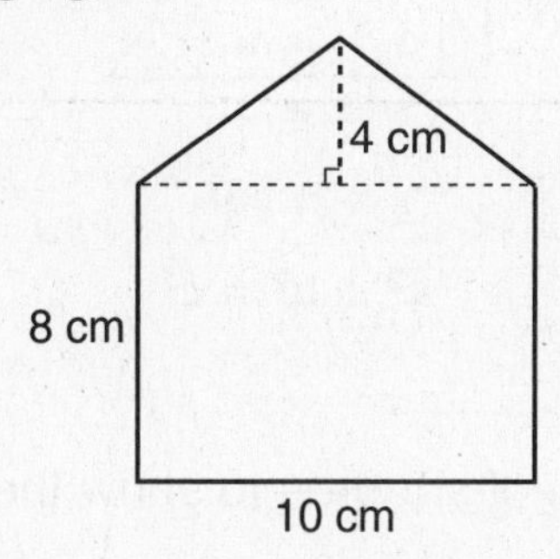

A 96 cm^2

B 100 cm^2

C 112 cm^2

D 120 cm^2

---

6. The world's largest Ferris wheel was built in London in 1897. The wheel had a radius of 150 feet. About how far would you travel in one turn of this wheel?

F 300 feet

G 470 feet

H 950 feet

J 1900 feet

Lesson 11: Coordinate Geometry

In this lesson, you will find the distance between two points and the midpoint of two points on a coordinate plane. You will also verify characteristics of geometric figures on a coordinate plane.

The Pythagorean Theorem

The **Pythagorean theorem** is derived using the coordinate plane. The theorem states that for any right triangle, the square of the length of the hypotenuse is equal to the sum of the squares of the lengths of the legs.

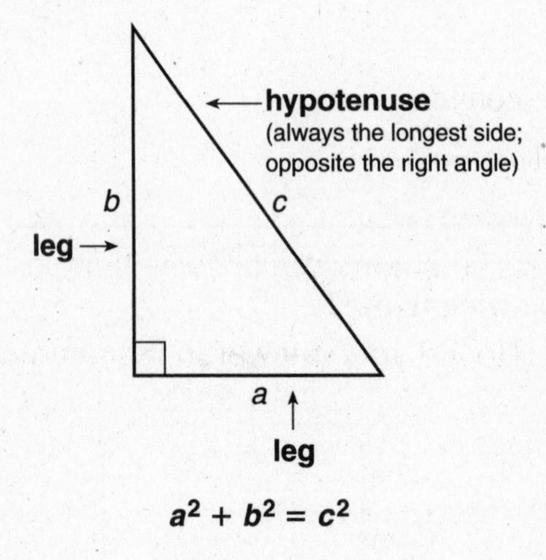

$$a^2 + b^2 = c^2$$

The following model uses sides of squares to show the Pythagorean theorem.

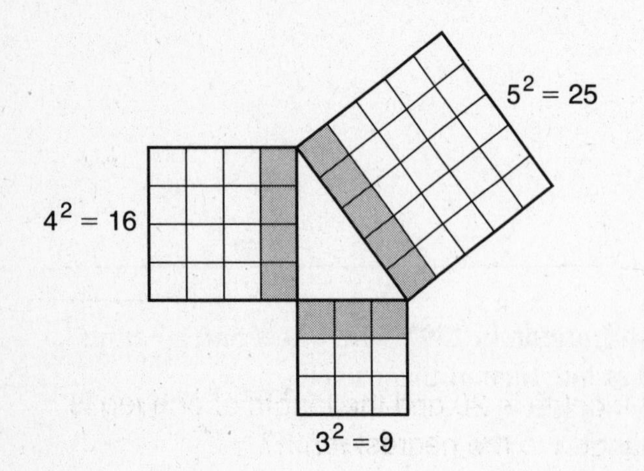

$$a^2 + b^2 = c^2$$

$$3^2 + 4^2 = 5^2$$

$$9 + 16 = 25$$

$$25 = 25$$

Objectives: 4b **DOK 2**

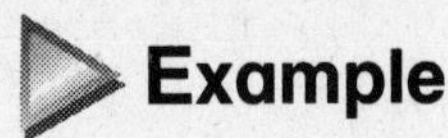

Example

What is the value of *b* in the following right triangle?

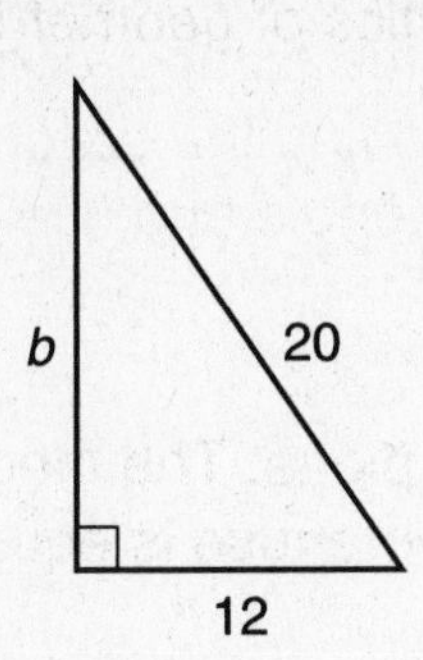

$$a^2 + b^2 = c^2$$
$$12^2 + b^2 = 20^2$$
$$144 + b^2 = 400$$
$$b^2 = 400 - 144$$
$$b^2 = 256$$
$$b = \sqrt{256}$$
$$b = 16$$

The value of *b* is 16 units.

Practice

Directions: Use the Pythagorean theorem to answer Numbers 1 through 3.

1. What is the value of *b*? (Round your answer to the nearest hundredth.)

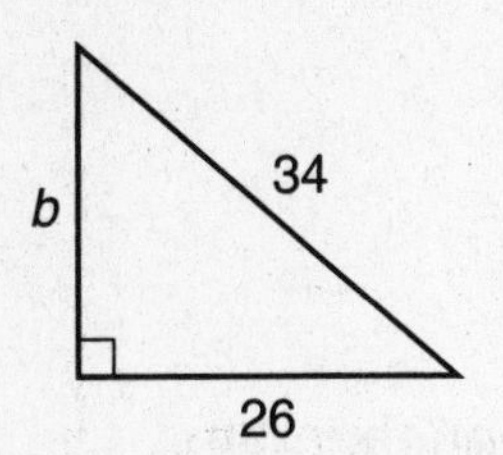

$b =$ __________

2. What is the value of *c*?

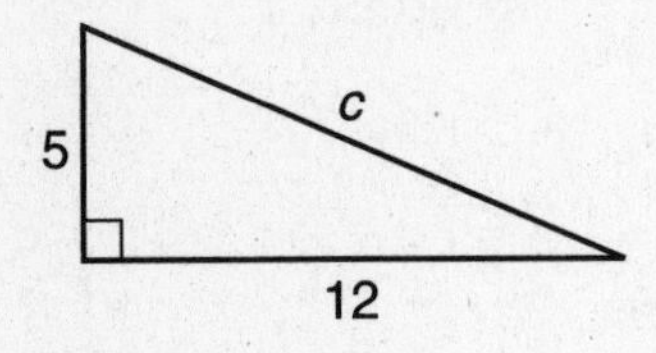

$c =$ __________

3. If the length of the hypotenuse of a right triangle is 20 and the length of one leg is 10, what is the length of the other leg rounded to the nearest tenth?

A. 10.0

B. 13.7

C. 15.0

D. 17.3

Distance Between Points

Two points have the coordinates (x_1, y_1) and (x_2, y_2). To find the distance, *d*, between two points with the same *y*-coordinate, find the absolute value of the difference of their *x*-coordinates. To find the distance between two points with the same *x*-coordinate, find the absolute value of the difference of their *y*-coordinates. To find the distance between two points with different *x*- and *y*-coordinates, draw a right triangle and use the Pythagorean theorem.

Example

What is the length of $\overline{AC}$?

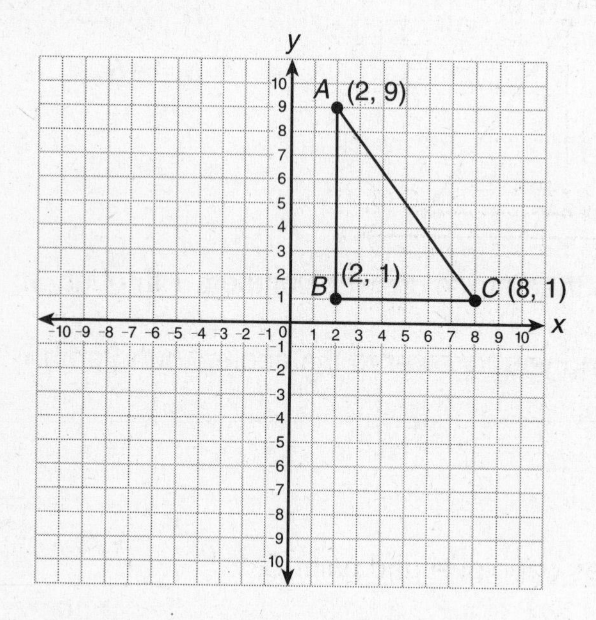

First, find the lengths of $\overline{AB}$ and $\overline{BC}$.

AB (read "the length of $\overline{AB}$") $= |y_2 - y_1| = |9 - 1| = 8$ units

BC (read "the length of $\overline{BC}$") $= |x_2 - x_1| = |8 - 2| = 6$ units

Use the Pythagorean theorem to find *AC*.

$$(AB)^2 + (BC)^2 = (AC)^2$$

$$8^2 + 6^2 = (AC)^2$$

$$100 = (AC)^2$$

$$\sqrt{100} = \sqrt{(AC)^2}$$

$$10 = AC$$

The length of $\overline{AC}$ is 10 units.

Objectives: 4b

Another way to find the distance from point A (x_1, y_1) to point C (x_2, y_2) in the previous example is to use the distance formula. The distance formula is derived from the Pythagorean theorem.

$$d = \sqrt{(x_2 - x_1)^2 + (y_2 - y_1)^2}$$

Example

Use the distance formula to find the length of $\overline{AC}$.

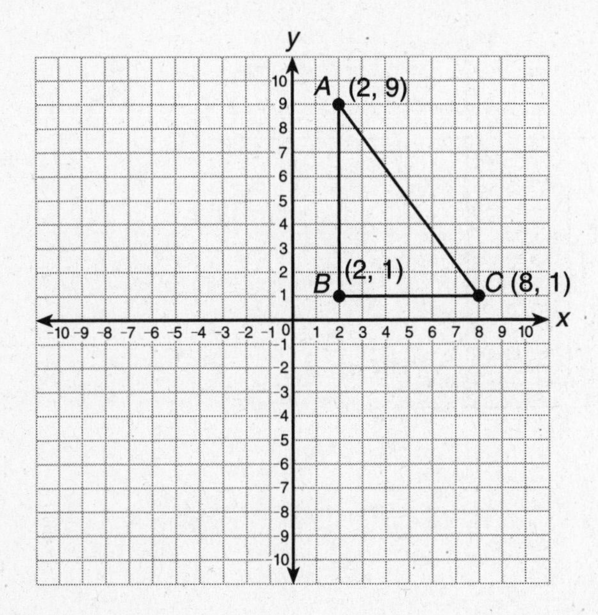

First, find the coordinates of point A and point C.

A: (2, 9) C: (8, 1)

Substitute the values into the distance formula and simplify.

$$AC = \sqrt{(x_2 - x_1)^2 + (y_2 - y_1)^2}$$

$$= \sqrt{(8 - 2)^2 + (1 - 9)^2}$$

$$= \sqrt{6^2 + (-8)^2}$$

$$= \sqrt{100}$$

$$= 10$$

The length of $\overline{AC}$ is 10 units.

Practice

Directions: For Numbers 1 through 4, use the distance formula to find the length of each side of parallelogram *ABCD*. Round your answers to the nearest tenth.

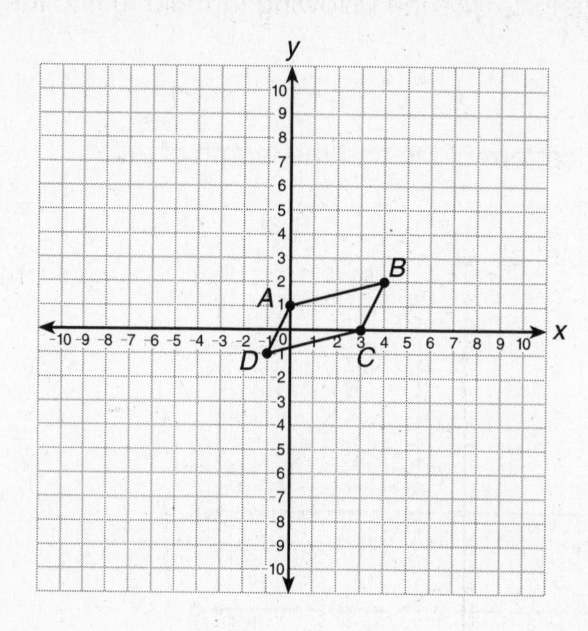

1. *AB* = ____________________

2. *DC* = ____________________

3. *AD* = ____________________

4. *BC* = ____________________

5. If you draw diagonal $\overline{BD}$, what will be its approximate length?

   A. 3.2 units

   B. 4.2 units

   C. 5.1 units

   D. 5.8 units

Objectives: 4b

Midpoint

The **midpoint**, ***M***, is the point that divides a segment into two equal segments. Two points have the coordinates (x_1, y_1) and (x_2, y_2). Think of the midpoint as the average of the two endpoints. Use the following formula to find the midpoint of a segment.

$$M = \left(\frac{x_1 + x_2}{2}, \frac{y_1 + y_2}{2}\right)$$

Example

Find the midpoint of $\overline{AZ}$.

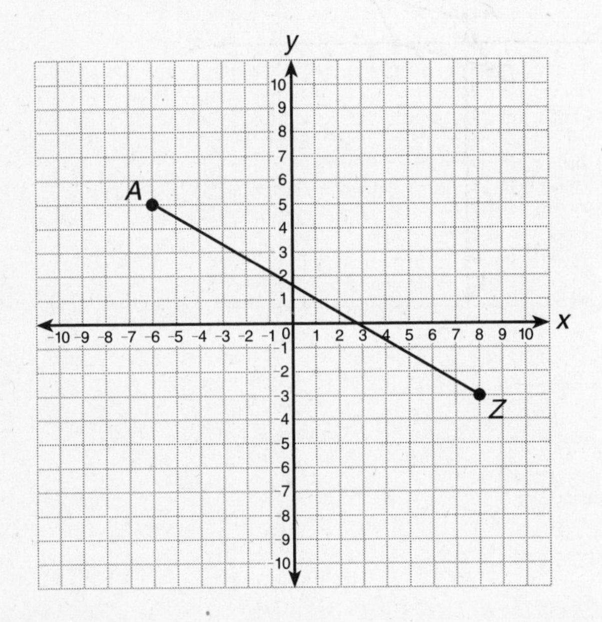

First, find the coordinates of point *A* and point *Z*.

A: (−6, 5)   *Z*: (8, −3)

Substitute the values into the midpoint formula and simplify.

$$M = \left(\frac{x_1 + x_2}{2}, \frac{y_1 + y_2}{2}\right)$$

$$= \left(\frac{-6 + 8}{2}, \frac{5 + (-3)}{2}\right)$$

$$= \left(\frac{2}{2}, \frac{2}{2}\right)$$

$$= (1, 1)$$

The midpoint of $\overline{AZ}$ is (1, 1).

Practice

Directions: For Numbers 1 through 4, use the midpoint formula to find the midpoint of each side of parallelogram *ABCD*.

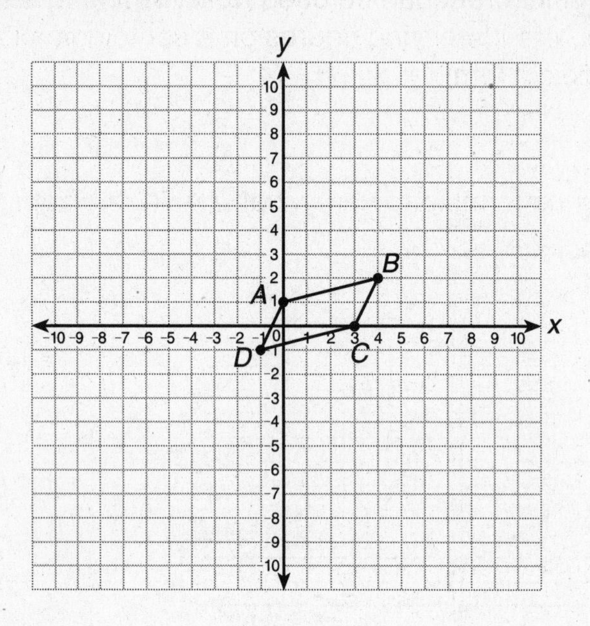

1. $\overline{AB}$ ______________________

2. $\overline{AD}$ ______________________

3. $\overline{BC}$ ______________________

4. $\overline{CD}$ ______________________

5. If you draw diagonal $\overline{BD}$, what will be its midpoint?

   A. (1, 0)

   B. $\left(1\frac{1}{2}, \frac{1}{2}\right)$

   C. $\left(1\frac{1}{2}, 1\frac{1}{2}\right)$

   D. $\left(2\frac{1}{2}, 1\frac{1}{2}\right)$

Objectives: 4b

Identifying Triangles

You can use the distance formula to find each side length of a triangle on a coordinate plane. Then, you can identify whether the triangle is isosceles, equilateral, or scalene. Finally, the Pythagorean theorem can be used to determine whether the triangle is a right triangle. When you are identifying figures on a coordinate plane, it is easiest to leave the answers in radical form.

Example

Use the distance formula to verify that $\triangle ABC$ is a right scalene triangle.

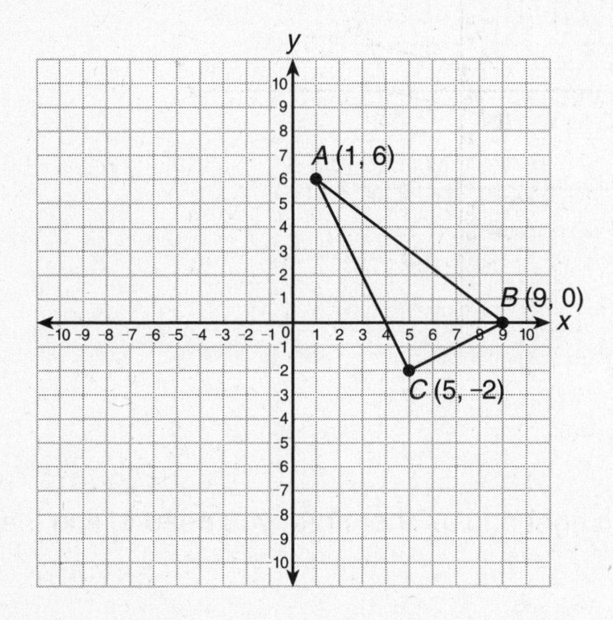

Use the distance formula to find the length of each side.

$$AC = \sqrt{(5 - 1)^2 + (-2 - 6)^2} = \sqrt{80}$$

$$BC = \sqrt{(5 - 9)^2 + (-2 - 0)^2} = \sqrt{20}$$

$$AB = \sqrt{(9 - 1)^2 + (0 - 6)^2} = \sqrt{100}$$

Since there are no congruent sides, $\triangle ABC$ is scalene.

Substitute the side lengths into the Pythagorean theorem.

$$a^2 + b^2 = c^2$$

$$(\sqrt{80})^2 + (\sqrt{20})^2 = (\sqrt{100})^2$$

$$100 = 100$$

Since the side lengths make the equation true, $\triangle ABC$ is also a right triangle.

You can also use the slope formula to determine whether a triangle is a right triangle. Remember that two lines are perpendicular if their slopes are opposite reciprocals. If you need to review this topic, it is located in Lesson 9.

Example

Use the slope formula to verify that $\triangle ABC$ is a right triangle.

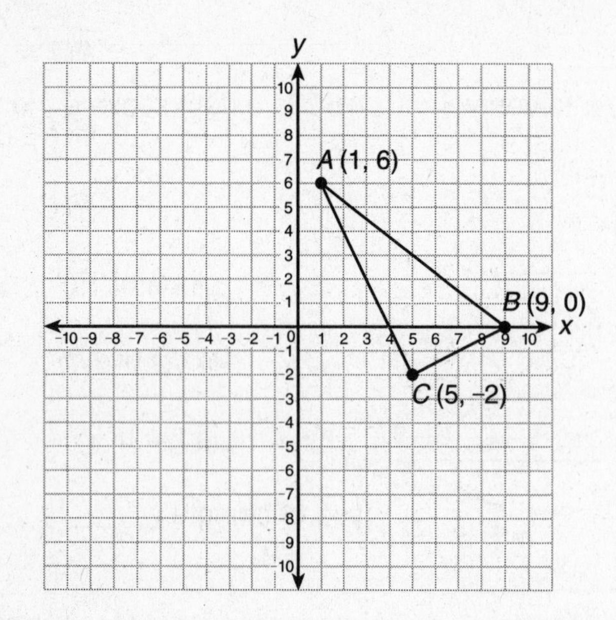

Angle C looks like it is a right angle. Therefore, you need to find the slopes of $\overline{AC}$ and $\overline{BC}$.

$$\text{slope} = \frac{y_2 - y_1}{x_2 - x_1}$$

$$\text{slope of } \overline{AC} = \frac{-2 - 6}{5 - 1} = \frac{-8}{4} = -2$$

$$\text{slope of } \overline{BC} = \frac{-2 - 0}{5 - 9} = \frac{-2}{-4} = \frac{1}{2}$$

Since the slope of $\overline{AC}$ is the opposite reciprocal of the slope of $\overline{BC}$, $\overline{AC}$ is perpendicular to $\overline{BC}$. Therefore, $\angle C$ is a right angle, and $\triangle ABC$ is a right triangle.

Practice

1. Use the distance formula and the slope formula to identify whether the triangle is right, scalene, isosceles, equilateral, or some combination of these. Leave your answers in radical form.

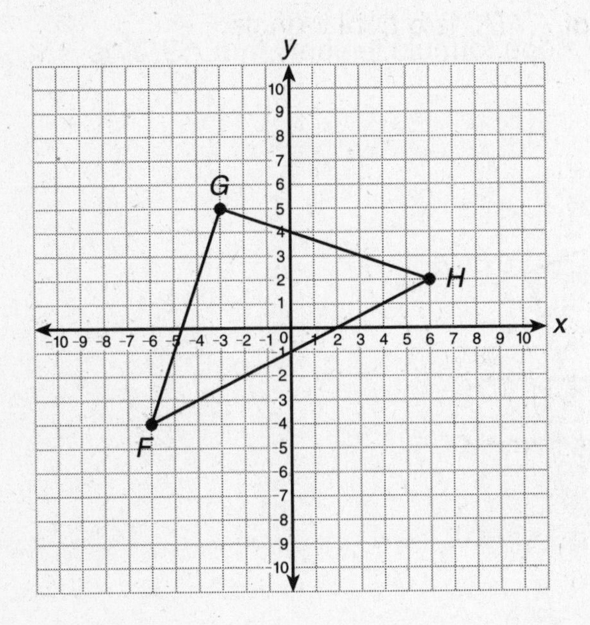

$FG =$ ________

$GH =$ ________

$FH =$ ________

slope of $\overline{FG} =$ ________

slope of $\overline{GH} =$ ________

slope of $\overline{FH} =$ ________

type of triangle ________________

2. Use the distance formula and the Pythagorean theorem to identify whether the triangle is right, scalene, isosceles, equilateral, or some combination of these. Leave your answers in radical form. Justify your answer by showing your work involving the Pythagorean theorem.

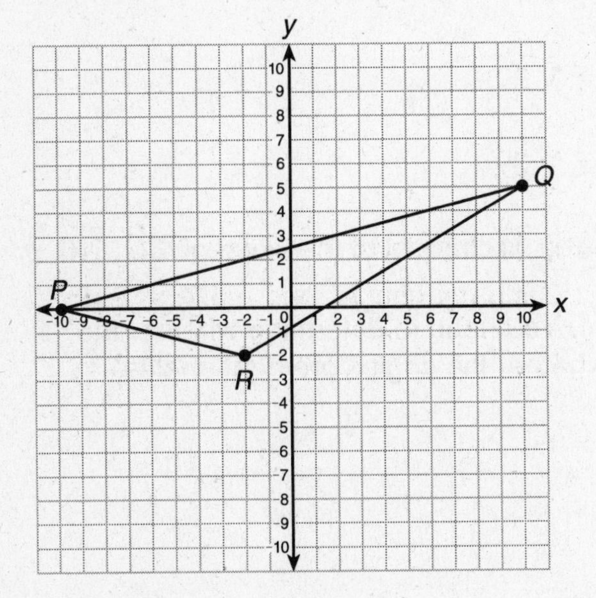

$PQ =$ ________

$QR =$ ________

$PR =$ ________

Pythagorean theorem true? ________

type of triangle ________________

Identifying Quadrilaterals

You can use both the distance formula and the slope formula to identify quadrilaterals on a coordinate plane.

Example

Use the distance formula and the slope formula to verify that *ABCD* is a square.

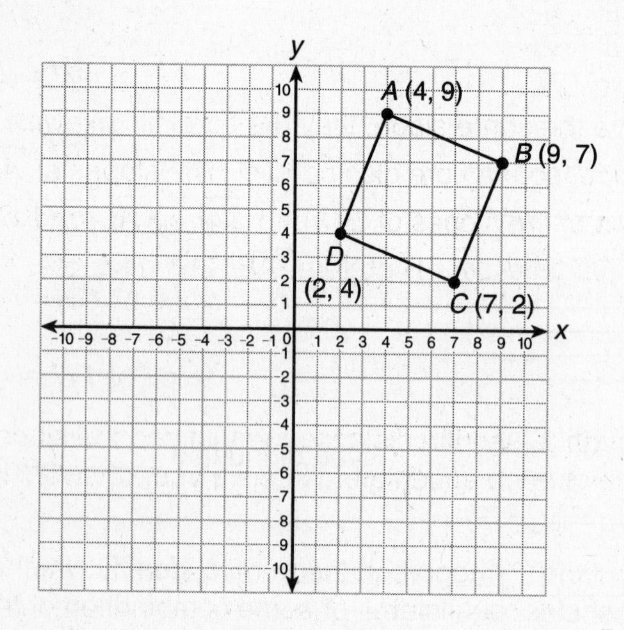

Use the distance formula to find the length of each side.

$$AB = \sqrt{(9 - 4)^2 + (7 - 9)^2} = \sqrt{29}$$

$$BC = \sqrt{(7 - 9)^2 + (2 - 7)^2} = \sqrt{29}$$

$$CD = \sqrt{(7 - 2)^2 + (2 - 4)^2} = \sqrt{29}$$

$$DA = \sqrt{(2 - 4)^2 + (4 - 9)^2} = \sqrt{29}$$

The side lengths are all congruent. You need to determine whether the opposite sides are parallel, and whether the angles are right angles.

Use the slope formula to find the slope of each segment.

slope of $\overline{AB} = \frac{7 - 9}{9 - 4} = -\frac{2}{5}$

slope of $\overline{BC} = \frac{2 - 7}{7 - 9} = \frac{5}{2}$

slope of $\overline{CD} = \frac{4 - 2}{2 - 7} = -\frac{2}{5}$

slope of $\overline{DA} = \frac{9 - 4}{4 - 2} = \frac{5}{2}$

Since $\overline{AB}$ and $\overline{CD}$ have the same slope, they are parallel. Likewise, $\overline{BC}$ and $\overline{DA}$ have the same slope, so they are also parallel. The slopes of $\overline{AB}$ and $\overline{CD}$ are opposite reciprocals of the slopes of $\overline{BC}$ and $\overline{DA}$, so $\overline{AB}$ and $\overline{CD}$ are each perpendicular to $\overline{BC}$ and $\overline{DA}$. Therefore, *ABCD* is a square.

Practice

Directions: For Numbers 1 through 3, use the distance formula and the slope formula to identify the most specific name of each quadrilateral. Leave your answers in radical form.

1.

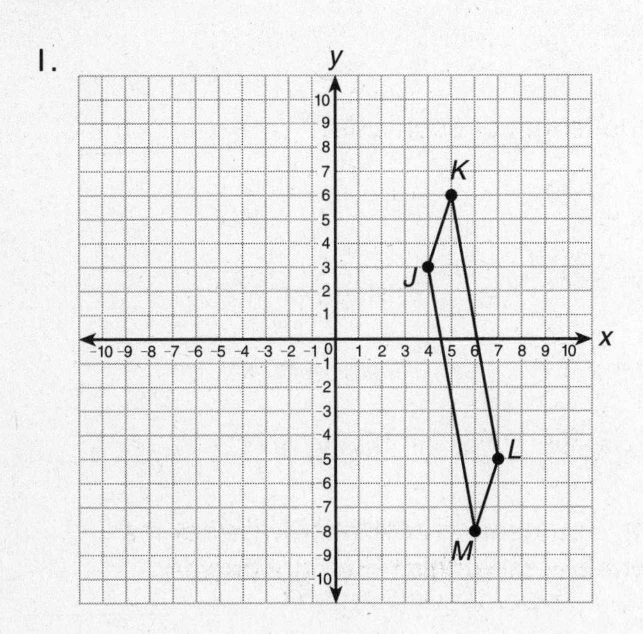

$JK =$ __________

$KL =$ __________

$LM =$ __________

$JM =$ __________

slope of $\overline{JK} =$ __________

slope of $\overline{KL} =$ __________

slope of $\overline{LM} =$ __________

slope of $\overline{JM} =$ __________

type of quadrilateral _______________

2.

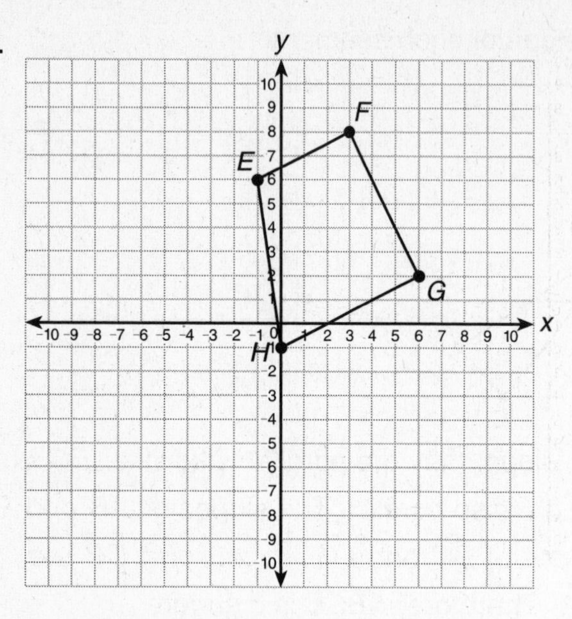

$EF =$ ________

$FG =$ ________

$GH =$ ________

$EH =$ ________

slope of $\overline{EF} =$ ________

slope of $\overline{FG} =$ ________

slope of $\overline{GH} =$ ________

slope of $\overline{EH} =$ ________

type of quadrilateral ________

3.

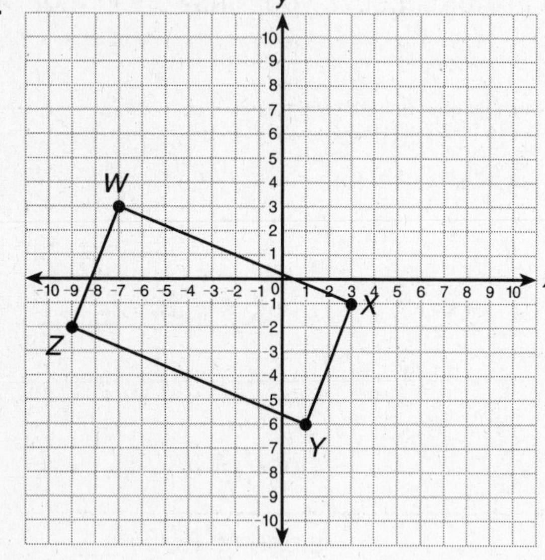

$WX =$ ________

$XY =$ ________

$YZ =$ ________

$WZ =$ ________

slope of $\overline{WX} =$ ________

slope of $\overline{XY} =$ ________

slope of $\overline{YZ} =$ ________

slope of $\overline{WZ} =$ ________

type of quadrilateral ________

SATP Practice begins on the following page.

Directions: Use the following coordinate plane to answer Numbers 1 through 3.

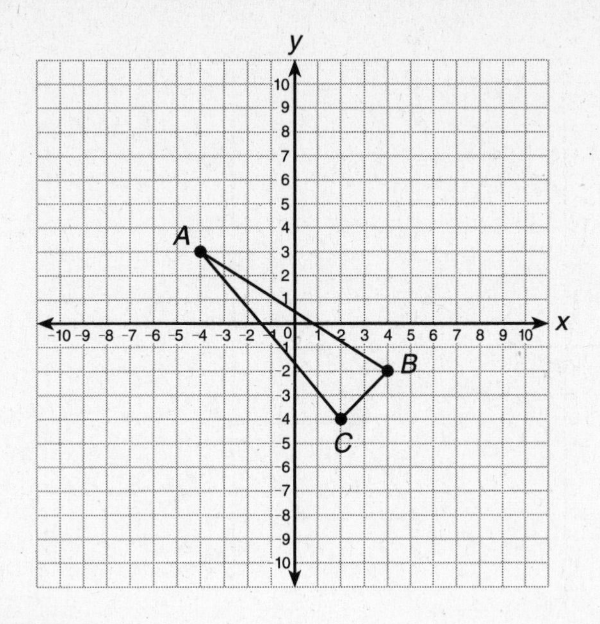

1. Which statement is TRUE?

A $\overline{AB}$ is congruent to $\overline{AC}$.

B $\overline{AC}$ is perpendicular to $\overline{BC}$.

C $AB = \sqrt{93}$

D $BC = \sqrt{8}$

---

2. What is the midpoint of $\overline{AC}$?

F $\left(-1, -\frac{1}{2}\right)$

G $\left(-\frac{1}{2}, -1\right)$

H $(-2, -1)$

J $(-1, -2)$

---

3. What type of triangle is $\triangle ABC$?

A Scalene

B Isosceles

C Equilateral

D Right and scalene

Directions: Use the following coordinate plane to answer Numbers 4 through 6.

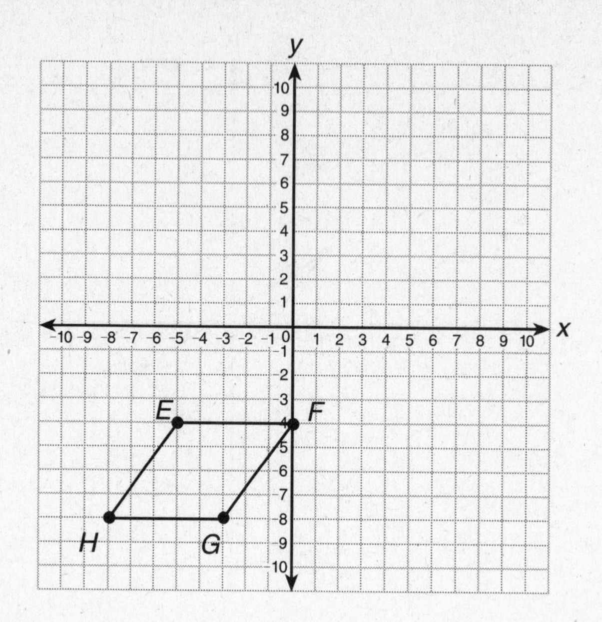

4. Which statement is NOT true?

F $\overline{EF}$ is parallel to $\overline{GH}$.

G $\overline{FG}$ is parallel to $\overline{EH}$.

H $\overline{FG}$ is perpendicular to $\overline{GH}$.

J $\overline{EF}$, $\overline{FG}$, $\overline{GH}$, and $\overline{EH}$ are congruent.

---

5. What is the slope of $\overline{EH}$?

A $-\frac{4}{3}$

B $-\frac{3}{4}$

C $\frac{3}{4}$

D $\frac{4}{3}$

---

6. What is the most specific name for quadrilateral *EFGH*?

F Square

G Rhombus

H Trapezoid

J Parallelogram

Data Analysis and Probability

Statistics are invaluable when making decisions based on data sets. The Mississippi Department of Transportation may base a decision about whether to repave a road on the number of vehicles that use that road on a weekly basis. Newspapers and magazines frequently use graphs to present some aspect of the news, such as how the government is spending tax dollars or how the season's top movies compare at the box office.

In this unit, you will interpret and summarize a set of experimental data presented in a scatterplot. You will also write the equation for the line of best fit and use the equation to make predictions about data represented in scatterplots.

In This Unit

Lesson 12: Data Analysis

In this lesson, you will use scatterplots to make predictions and you will find the line of best fit for a given data set.

Scatterplots

A **scatterplot** is used to show how two data sets are related. The data values are plotted as ordered pairs and then observed to see how closely they come to forming a straight line.

Example

The following table shows the number of hours Juanita studied for each of her first seven algebra tests and the grade she received on each test.

Grade Versus Study Time

Study Time (in hours)	1.5	3.0	1.0	2.5	1.5	3.5	4.0
Grade	80	90	70	88	85	95	98

This is how the data look in a scatterplot.

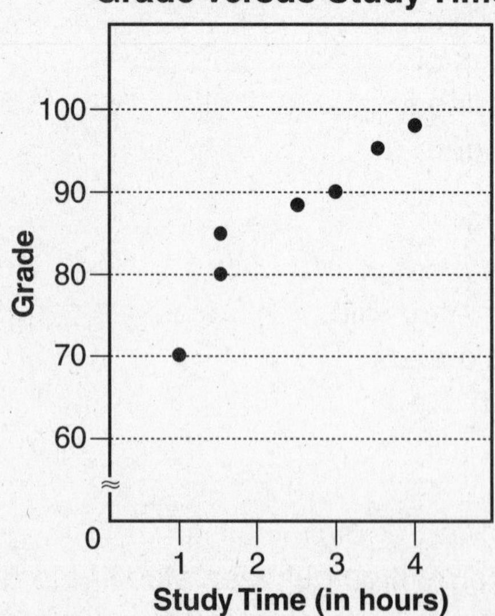

The scatterplot shows that the data points come close to forming a straight line. The more hours Juanita studied, the higher the grade she received on the test. This relationship is **direct:** as one quantity increases, the other quantity increases. Relationships can also be **inverse:** as one quantity increases, the other quantity decreases.

Objectives: 5a, 5b

Correlation and Trend Lines

When two data sets are related, we say they are **correlated**. A direct relationship represents a **positive correlation**. An inverse relationship represents a **negative correlation**. The closer the data points come to forming a straight line, the more strongly they are correlated. When the data points lie in a straight line, the data sets have **perfect correlation**. Two data sets that have no relationship have **no correlation**.

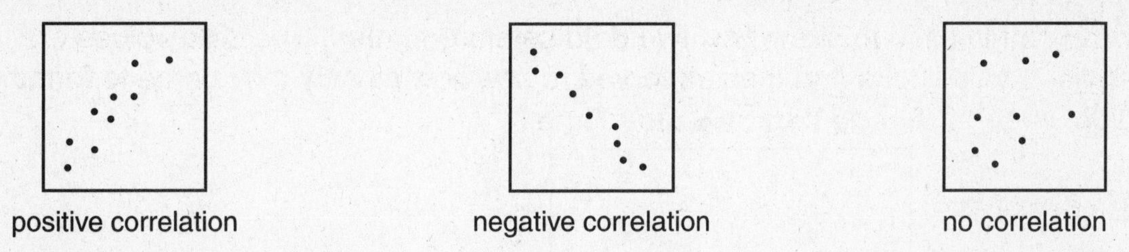

When data sets show a positive or negative correlation, a **line of best fit** can be drawn to approximate missing data. A line of best fit has close to the same number of data points above as it does below.

Example

Here is the scatterplot from the previous page with a line of best fit drawn through the data.

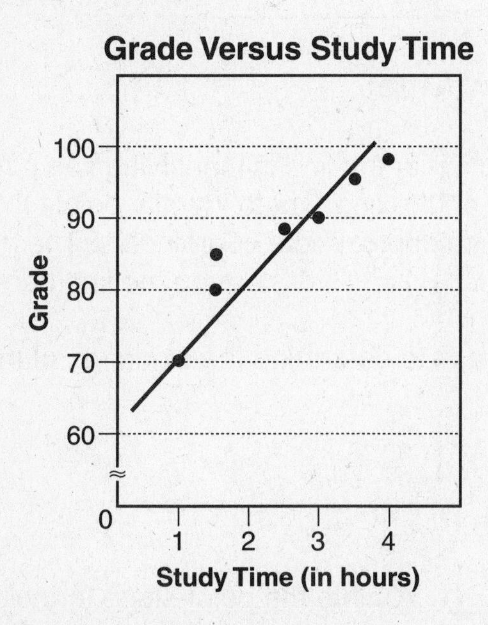

The scatterplot shows a positive correlation between study time and grade. A line of best fit has been drawn through the data points in order to make predictions about missing values. Looking at the line of best fit, it appears that if Juanita studies for 2 hours, she will receive a grade of about 80. (This is a prediction, since the table does not include a study time of 2.0 hours.)

Finding the Equation of the Line of Best Fit by Hand

Once the line of best fit is drawn on a scatterplot, you can find its equation using the skills you reviewed in Lesson 4. You can use the equation of the line of best fit to make predictions for different values.

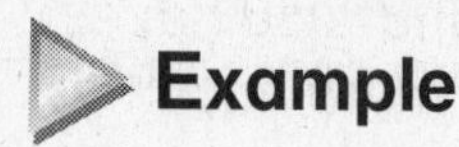

Example

What is the equation of the line of best fit from the previous example?

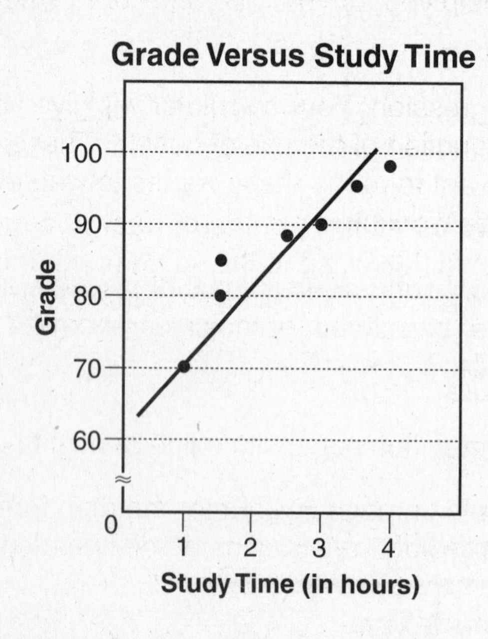

The first step in finding the equation of the line is identifying two points, with coordinates (x_1, y_1) and (x_2, y_2), on the line. Try to identify points that are easy to work with. You may have to use approximate coordinates. The point $(x_1, y_1) = (1, 70)$ and the point $(x_2, y_2) = (2, 80)$ are on the line above.

Use the points on the line of best fit to determine the slope, m, of the line.

$$m = \frac{y_2 - y_1}{x_2 - x_1} = \frac{80 - 70}{2 - 1} = \frac{10}{1} = 10$$

The slope of the line of best fit is 10.

Substitute $m = 10$ and $(x_1, y_1) = (1, 70)$ into the point-slope formula and solve for y.

$$y - y_1 = m(x - x_1)$$

$$y - 70 = 10(x - 1)$$

$$y = 10x + 60$$

The equation of the line of best fit is $y = 10x + 60$.

Objectives: 5a, 5b

Finding the Equation of the Line of Best Fit Using a Calculator

You can enter the data values from a table and then find the equation of the line of best fit by using a graphing calculator. You need to be very careful when entering the values into your calculator. It is always a good idea to double check the values after you have entered them. This method of finding the equation of the line of best fit is more accurate than by hand. The process for doing this will be different depending on which calculator you use. Your teacher should be able to help you, or you can read your owner's manual if you don't know how to do this.

This process is called finding the linear regression. Your calculator will give you the value of the slope and *y*-intercept of the equation of the line of best fit. These numbers will rarely come out as integers. You will want to round these values to whatever place value is reasonable for the problem you are working on.

Your calculator may also give you values for r and r^2. The value of r^2 will always be between 0 and 1. The stronger the data are correlated, or the closer the data are to forming a straight line, the closer r^2 will be to 1.

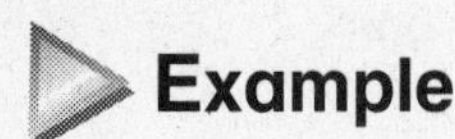

Example

Here is the table from the example on page 212. Enter the data from the table into a graphing calculator and then find the equation of the line of best fit.

Grade Versus Study Time

Study Time (in hours)	1.5	3.0	1.0	2.5	1.5	3.5	4.0
Grade	80	90	70	88	85	95	98

In this example rounding to the nearest tenth is reasonable. Your graphing calculator should give you a slope of 7.8 and a *y*-intercept of 67.6.

The equation of the line of best fit is $y = 7.8x + 67.6$. You can see that this equation is different than the equation you found by hand. You can graph the data points, the equation you found by hand, and the equation you just found on your calculator and compare the two lines.

Use the equation of the line of best fit from your calculator to predict Juanita's score if she studies for 2 hours.

The prediction is 83.2 using this equation. This is slightly higher than the prediction of 80 from the line of best fit drawn by hand.

Objectives: 5a, 5b **DOK 3**

Practice

Directions: Write whether each scatterplot in Numbers 1 through 4 shows positive, negative, or no correlation. If the scatterplot shows positive or negative correlation, draw a line of best fit and make the given prediction.

1.

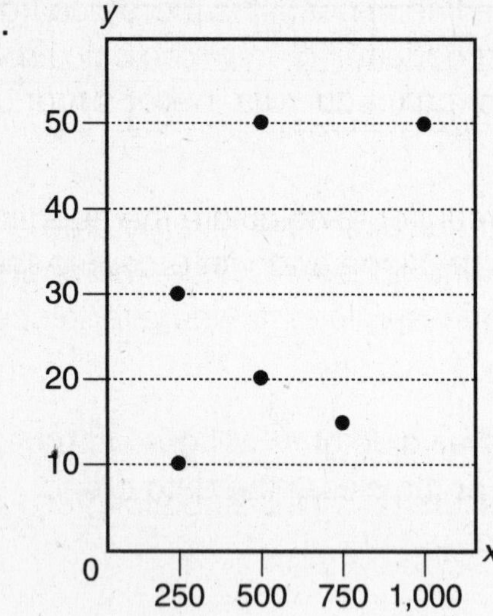

correlation ____________________

prediction for y when x is 300

____

2.

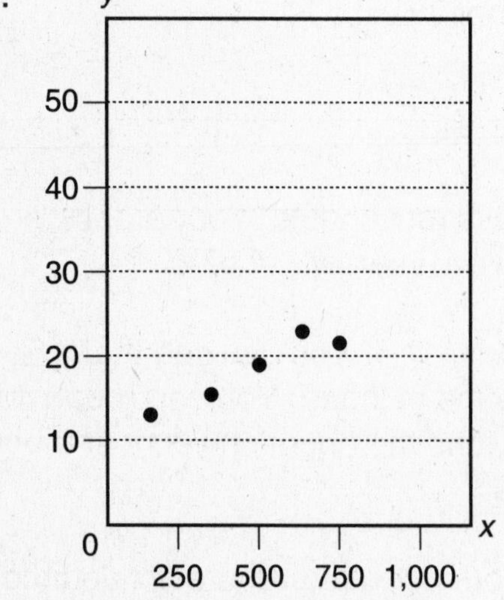

correlation ____________________

prediction for y when x is 1,000

____

3.

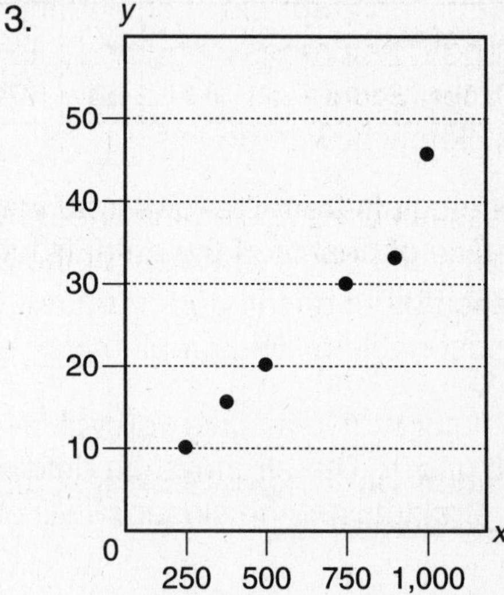

correlation ____________________

prediction for y when x is 600

____

4.

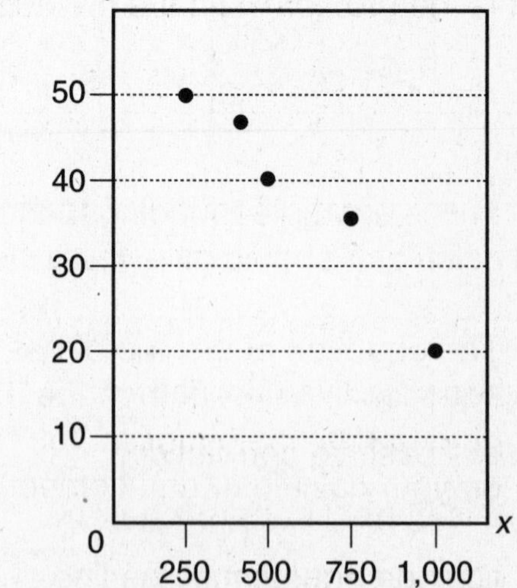

correlation ____________________

prediction for y when x is 850

____

Objectives: 5a, 5b **DOK 3**

Directions: Use the following information to answer Numbers 5 through 9.

The following table shows the number of hours of sleep a group of algebra students got the night before a test and each student's score as a percent.

Math Score Versus Hours of Sleep

Hours of Sleep	9	4	7	6	6	8	9	8	5	7	8	7
Math Test Score	93	71	84	77	82	93	91	100	70	83	90	90

5. Use the points from the table and your graphing calculator to calculate the equation of the line of best fit of the data. Round your values for slope and *y*-intercept to the nearest tenth.

 ____

6. If a student got 2 hours of sleep, predict his or her score using the equation you found in Number 5.

 ____

7. If a student got 11 hours of sleep, predict his or her score using the equation you found in Number 5.

 ____

8. What is the problem with the prediction from Number 7?

 ____

 ____

9. Which statement about the data is **true**?

 A. It has negative correlation.

 B. It has positive correlation.

 C. It has perfect correlation.

 D. It has no correlation.

Directions: Use the following information to answer Numbers 10 through 14.

The following scatterplot shows the data from the table on the previous page.

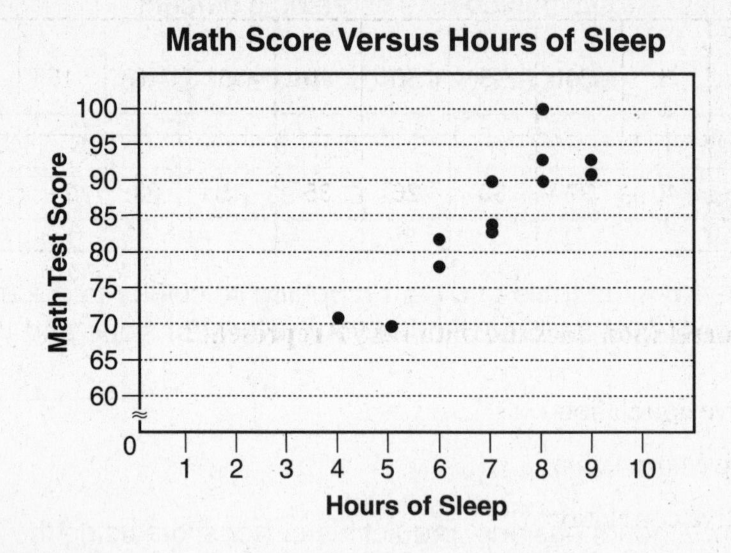

10. Draw a line of best fit through the data on the scatterplot.

11. Use two points on the line of best fit you drew for Number 10 to calculate the line of best fit of the data. Be sure to write down which two points you used to find the equation.

____

12. If a student got 2 hours of sleep, predict his or her score using the equation you found in Number 11.

____

13. If a student got 10 hours of sleep, predict his or her score using the equation you found in Number 11.

____

14. If a student scored 75 on the test, guess how many hours of sleep he or she got the night before the test.

____

 SATP Practice begins on the following page.

Directions: Use the following information and scatterplot to answer Numbers 1 through 3.

The following table shows the number of miles a group of students ran in the month before running a 5-mile race and each student's race time.

Race Time Versus Practice Length

Practice Length (in miles)	5	20	15	30	10	35	18	15	25	22
Race Time (in minutes)	40	27	30	26	35	23	29	24	25	31

1. What type of correlation does the data BEST represent?

A Weak positive correlation

B Weak negative correlation

C Strong positive correlation

D Strong negative correlation

---

2. What is the BEST representation of the equation of the line of best fit of the data?

F $y = -0.5x + 38$

G $y = 0.4x + 38$

H $y = 0.6x + 38$

J $y = -0.8x + 38$

---

3. What is the BEST prediction of the number of miles a student practiced if he took 30 minutes to run the 5-mile race?

A 11 miles

B 14 miles

C 17 miles

D 20 miles

Directions: Use the following information and scatterplot to answer Numbers 4 and 5.

The scatterplot and line of best fit below represent the T-shirt sales of the Greenville High School Band this year.

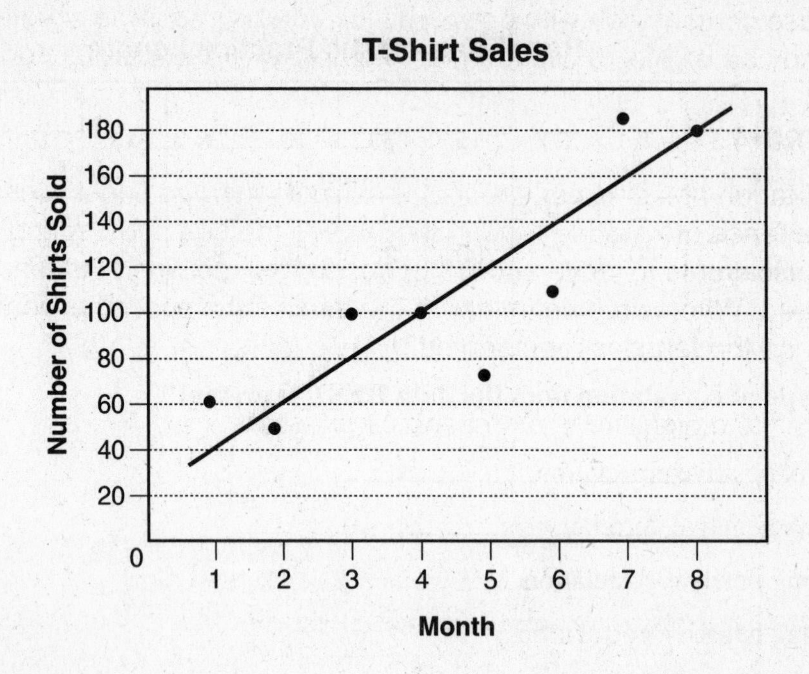

4. What is the BEST representation of the equation of the line of best fit in the scatterplot above?

F $y = 0.05x - 1$

G $y = 0.05x + 99.8$

H $y = 20x + 196$

J $y = 20x + 20$

---

5. What is the BEST prediction of the number of T-shirts that will be sold in month 9.

A 180

B 200

C 220

D 240
